Common Core
Writing Companion

GRADE 8

Perfection Learning®

EDITORIAL DIRECTOR: CAROL FRANCIS

EXECUTIVE EDITOR: JIM STRICKLER

EDITOR: ANDREA STARK

PROOFREADING COORDINATOR: SHERI COOPER

ART DIRECTOR: RANDY MESSER

DESIGNER: TOBI CUNNINGHAM

COVER: MIKE ASPENGREN

REVIEWERS: AMY HALLAS
                           JUNIOR HIGH LANGUAGE ARTS AND LITERATURE TEACHER
                           OUR LADY OF GUADALUPE SCHOOL
                           OXNARD SCHOOL DISTRICT
                           OXNARD, CALIFORNIA

                           GLENDA WEBER
                           LITERACY COACH UMATILLA HIGH SCHOOL
                           LAKE COUNTRY SCHOOL DISTRICT
                           UMATILLA, FLORIDA

PHOTO CREDITS: istockphoto.com: pp. 19, 36; photos.com: pp. 4, 22, 50, 58, 60, 90, 94, 100

91102
ISBN: 978-0-7891-8461-0

Printed in the United States of America

Table of Contents

Table of Contents *continued*

Meeting the Common Core State Standards

The Common Core State Standards declare the importance of writing to texts—of drawing knowledge from sources and using what you learn to help you express your ideas clearly:

> For students, writing is a key means of asserting and defending claims, showing what they know about a subject, and conveying what they have experienced, imagined, thought, and felt.

The instruction and activities in this book will prepare you to meet the standards. If you do, you will score well on the assessments based on them.

What Are the Characteristics of Good Writing?

Your writing will be evaluated according to how well it shows the basic characteristics found in all types of good writing:

- *Development:* Does the text state the key idea clearly and support it strongly?
- *Organization:* Does the text include an introduction, body, and conclusion? Are transitions from one idea to another smooth and logical?
- *Evidence:* Is the information in the text relevant and strong?
- *Language and Style:* Does the text use words precisely? Is the tone appropriate?
- *Grammar, Spelling, and Punctuation:* Does the text use standard grammar, spelling, and punctuation?

How Is This Book Organized?

The first chapter of this book provides instruction and activities to help develop the characteristics of good writing listed above.

Each of the next five chapters focuses on a different type of writing.

- arguments
- informative/explanatory texts
- research reports
- literary analyses
- narratives

In each of these five chapters, the first several lessons highlight the elements particularly important to one type of writing. For example, the chapter on arguments includes lessons that focus on claims and counterclaims.

The next-to-last lesson in each chapter takes you, step-by-step, through writing a text. Built into these lessons are instruction and practice in grammar and usage that address the most common writing problems.

The final lesson in each chapter provides prompts for you to demonstrate your skills in gathering, analyzing, and using information in your writing. This lesson ends with a checklist based on the characteristics of good writing.

Chapter 1

Characteristics of Good Writing

No matter what type of writing you are asked to do, there are some common characteristics that all good writing shares. These are important for you to understand because your writing will be evaluated on these qualities.

> **Good writing**
> - is **well developed**
> - has a **cohesive organization**
> - contains **evidence** from sources to support main points
> - uses **precise language** and a formal **style**
> - follows rules of **standard grammar, spelling,** and **punctuation**

LESSON 1 DEVELOPMENT

Well-developed writing focuses on a main idea. This central idea is then expanded with interesting details, relevant facts, or carefully chosen evidence. The writer has a clear purpose that is appropriate to the task and the audience.

> **Purposes for Writing**
>
> Common writing purposes include informing, explaining, narrating a real or imagined story, and presenting an argument to convince readers.

Activity 1A *Finding the Main Idea*

Read the following paragraph and underline the main idea. Then answer the questions that follow.

> Our school could be improved by putting a salad bar in the cafeteria. A salad bar would offer students healthy foods. Fruits and vegetables contain many vitamins and are very nutritious. A salad bar would also offer students a light meal. Eating a heavy meal can bog students down and make it hard for them to stay awake in the afternoon. A salad would be satisfying without being too filling, so students could concentrate more on learning and less on staying awake. It would also offer students something different. A salad bar would make lunch a more pleasant experience for everyone!

1. What is the purpose of the passage?

_____

_____

2. How do the supporting details develop the main idea?

_____

_____

_____

_____

_____

3. Are the supporting details relevant and sufficient?

_____

_____

_____

_____

_____

> **Relevant and Sufficient**
> ....
> • Relevant details relate to the main idea.
> • Sufficient details mean there are enough details to answer the main questions the reader has about the topic.

Activity 1B Writing a Paragraph

Read the following facts about cyberbullying. Then complete the exercises below.

> ### Cyberbullying
>
> *Online bullying, called cyberbullying, happens when teens use the Internet, cell phones, or other devices to send or post text or images intended to hurt or embarrass another person. Cyberbullying is a problem that affects almost half of all American teens.*
>
> **How are teens cyberbullied? Some youth who cyberbully**
>
> • pretend they are other people online to trick others
>
> • spread lies and rumors about victims
>
> • trick people into revealing personal information
>
> • send or forward mean text messages
>
> • post pictures of victims without their consent

continued on next page

continued from previous page

When teens were asked why they think others cyberbully, 81 percent said that cyberbullies think it's funny. Other teens believe that youth who cyberbully

- don't think it's a big deal
- don't think about the consequences
- are encouraged by friends
- think everybody cyberbullies

How can I prevent cyberbullying?

- refuse to pass along cyberbullying messages
- tell friends to stop cyberbullying
- block communication with cyberbullies
- report cyberbullying to a trusted adult

1. Use the passage as a source of information for a paragraph of your own. Write a main idea statement for your paragraph.

_____

_____

_____

2. Go back to the passage and underline four details you can use to support your main idea statement.

3. Write a paragraph for an audience of students in 8th grade. Be sure your paragraph includes both your main idea statement and good supporting details. Put the information in your own words. Do not merely copy sentences from the passage.

_____

_____

_____

_____

_____

_____

Collaboration on Paragraphs

Use the following questions to evaluate a partner's paragraph:

- Is the purpose clear?
- Is the main idea well developed?
- Are there sufficient supporting details?

LESSON 2 ORGANIZATION

A well-organized piece of writing has a clear beginning, middle, and ending. It presents details in a logical order so that the reader can easily follow the ideas. Transitional words and phrases help the reader understand the relationship between ideas. The sentences fit together into paragraphs that clearly communicate the main idea.

Essay Organization

Most essays are organized using an introduction (beginning), a body (middle), and a conclusion (ending). The introduction and conclusion are one paragraph in length; the body is several paragraphs.

Organization	Used in	Transitional phrases
Chronological: time order	Narrative writing to explain events Informational/explanatory writing to explain steps in a process	*First, next, later, afterward, a few days later, at the same time*
Order of Importance: least to most important or most to least important	Argumentative writing to explain reasons Informational/explanatory writing to explain details	*First, another reason, however, on the other hand, finally*
Spatial Order: arranged according to location	Informational/explanatory writing to describe places and things	*In the upper corner, across, next to, under, beneath*
Comparison and Contrast: similarities and differences	Informational/explanatory writing to show how things are alike or different	*Similarly, in the same way, on the other hand, but, conversely*

Activity 2A Analyzing a Paragraph

Read the following passage. Then complete the exercises on the following page.

> Our school should institute a dress code of jeans and plain colored T-shirts. This is a good idea for several reasons. First, it will make it easier for principals and teachers to enforce the dress code. Right now, it is hard to tell if shorts are too short or shirts are too revealing. With a dress code, a teacher could tell at a glance if a student were wearing appropriate clothes. Secondly, if everyone wore the same thing, students would feel more equal. Rich kids and poor kids would be judged by their character, not by how they look. Finally, having a simple dress code would help students focus on their schoolwork, instead of their appearance. This could result in better grades and higher test scores. Changing the dress code to jeans and T-shirts would improve the learning experience for both the staff and students at our school.

1. Underline the main idea of the paragraph.

2. How are the main points organized? Refer to the chart on page 9 for organizational structures.

_____

3. Put parentheses around transitional words and phrases that help the reader make connections between the ideas.

Activity 2B Writing a Paragraph

You have decided to run for class president. Read the following list of responsibilities of the 8th grade class president. Then write a well-organized paragraph to an audience of your classmates explaining why they should elect you to the position. (You may make up some facts about yourself if needed.)

Requirements:

• must have a C + (78) or better grade in all current classes, an attendance record of 90 percent or better, and no suspensions

Expectations:

• attend weekly meetings Wednesday mornings before school

• plan dances, spirit days, and fund-raising events

• work with school administration to implement school policies

• advocate on behalf of all students to the administration and staff

Collaboration on Organization

Use the following questions to evaluate a partner's paragraph:

• Is the organization of the paragraph clear?

• Are appropriate transitional words and phrases used to connect ideas?

• Do the ideas flow in a logical order? Give your partner specific suggestions of how they can improve the organization of his or her paragraph. Revise your paragraphs on the basis of your partner's and your own evaluations.

_____

_____

_____

_____

_____

_____

_____

_____

_____

LESSON 3 EVIDENCE

Often you will be asked to read a text and then write about it. To support your ideas, you will be required to include evidence from the text in your writing. Textual evidence includes direct quotations and specific information from the text you read.

Activity 3A Analyzing a Paragraph

Read the following paragraph. Then complete the exercises below.

> In "The Hobbit" the character Bilbo Baggins is an unlikely hero, but he is still a hero. Physically, hobbits are short and have hairy feet. They don't usually travel or go on adventures. In chapter 1, Bilbo doesn't want to have any part of the adventure Gandalf offers. Bilbo says that adventures are "Nasty disturbing uncomfortable things! Make you late for dinner!" However, later he reluctantly agrees to set out with the dwarves. Throughout the story, Bilbo does some very heroic things. He outwits Gollum in a game of riddles, but he refuses to kill Gollum because he believes it would be unfair. In chapter 12, Bilbo enters Smaug the dragon's lair, alone. Even though he is afraid, he steals a cup and a jewel from the dragon. These courageous acts make Bilbo the hero of the story.

1. Underline three examples of textual evidence.

2. Is there adequate textual evidence to support the main idea? Why or why not?

_____

_____

_____

_____

_____

_____

_____

_____

Activity 3B Writing a Paragraph

Read the following excerpt. Then follow the directions below.

We have before us an ordeal of the most grievous kind. We have before us many, many long months of struggle and of suffering. You ask, what is our policy? I can say: It is to wage war, by sea, land and air, with all our might and with all the strength that God can give us; to wage war against a monstrous tyranny, never surpassed in the dark, lamentable catalogue of human crime. That is our policy. You ask, what is our aim? I can answer in one word: It is victory, victory at all costs, victory in spite of all terror, victory, however long and hard the road may be; for without victory, there is no survival. Let that be realised; no survival for the British Empire, no survival for all that the British Empire has stood for, no survival for the urge and impulse of the ages, that mankind will move forward towards its goal. But I take up my task with buoyancy and hope. I feel sure that our cause will not be suffered to fail among men. At this time I feel entitled to claim the aid of all, and I say, "come then, let us go forward together with our united strength.

—British Prime Minister Winston Churchill, from a speech given in 1940 during World War II

Write a paragraph explaining the relationship between courage and failure. Support your ideas using evidence from the passages above.

_____

_____

_____

_____

_____

_____

_____

_____

_____

_____

Collaboration on Evidence

Use the following questions to evaluate a partner's paragraph:

• Does the paragraph use evidence from the text?

• Is the evidence effective?

• Does it reinforce the writer's ideas?

• Give your partner specific details as you answer these questions. Revise your paragraphs on the basis of your partner's and your own evaluation.

LESSON 4 LANGUAGE AND STYLE

Good writing uses **language** that is precise and clear. Words are carefully chosen to help the reader "see" what is being described. Verbs are mostly active voice; nouns are specific, not trite. The **style** of the writing is formal, avoiding slang and personal pronouns.

> **Objective Tone**
>
> Notice how the paragraph below avoids giving opinions about the topic. The writing is factual and unbiased.

Activity 4A *Analyzing a Paragraph*

Read the following paragraph and underline four examples of clear, precise language.

> Inside everyone's chest is a beating heart. With each beat, this incredibly strong muscle pumps 2 ounces of blood throughout the body. Thump-thump. Blood flows into the heart's first chamber, the right atrium, from the veins. Thump-thump. The blood passes down into the right ventricle. Thump-thump. Out rushes the blood to the lungs where it is loaded up with oxygen. Thump-thump. Oxygen-rich blood enters the left atrium. Thump-thump. The strongest chamber, the left ventricle, pushes the blood out to deliver oxygen to the rest of the body.

Activity 4B *Writing a Paragraph*

Choose a topic you have studied recently in a science or history class. Write a paragraph that demonstrates clear, precise language and formal style.

_____

_____

_____

_____

_____

_____

_____

_____

_____

> **Collaboration on Evaluation**
>
> Use the following to evaluate a partner's paragraph:
>
> • Can you identify four or more examples of precise language?
>
> • Does the writing include interesting comparisons or figurative language?
>
> • Does it use a formal style and objective tone? Revise your paragraphs on the basis of your partner's and your own evaluations.

LESSON 5 CONVENTIONS IN WRITING

Using correct **grammar, spelling,** and **punctuation** is the finishing touch on an effective essay. Using verbs incorrectly, misspelling words, and using commas incorrectly can prevent your readers from understanding what you have written. For example, consider the sentence *Let's invite Amy my brother Jack and your dad.* Are Jack and the brother the same person or two different people? Commas can help the reader understand how many people to invite: *Let's invite Amy, my brother Jack, and your dad.*

Activity 5A Editing a Paragraph

Edit the paragraph for mistakes in grammar, spelling, and punctuation by rewriting it correctly on the lines below.

Many toys were invented by acident. During World War two, for example an engineer named Richard James wus trying to invent a spring that would help keep war ships level. One day, James acidentally knocks one of the springs to the floor. Surpringly, it bounces. And than moved end over end. That spring soon become the slinky, won of the hottest-selling toys of all time. In 1950, another Engineer was trying to invent something to replace reel rubber instead he produced a putty like material that bounced like rubber but snaped and broke when it was stretched. A few months later, Silly putty hits the markit. Sometimes people are more ingenus then they realize!

_____

_____

_____

_____

_____

_____

_____

_____

_____

_____

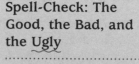

Spell-Check: The Good, the Bad, and the Ugly

If you use a computer to complete a writing assignment, you will probably have access to spell-check. (That's good!) However, don't assume that the computer will catch all of your errors. (That's bad!) Spell-check will not fined words witch are miss used butt spelled rite. (Ugly!)

Collaboration on Editing

Use the following to evaluate a partner's paragraph:

- Are all spelling errors corrected?

- Was a run-on sentence corrected?

- Are verb tenses consistent throughout the paragraph? Identify specific errors that should be corrected. Revise your paragraphs on the basis of your partner's and your own evaluations.

Writing an Argumentative Essay

How do you get people to agree with you? One way is to present them with an argument and support for it.

LESSON 1 CLAIMS

In an argumentative essay, you begin by making a claim. A **claim** is the main point you want readers to accept. It is more than just an opinion about a personal preference. It is a precise statement that you

- think is true
- can support with accurate and reasonable information
- expect some readers will disagree with; it is debatable

One example of a claim is, "All 8th grade students should be required to take a foreign language." Some people, but not all, will agree. Both supporters and opponents of it might back their claims with reasons that explain why students should be able to speak another language. Those against the idea might cite statistics that being proficient in reading and math are more important than learning a foreign language.

The claim in an argumentative essay almost always appears in the first paragraph. Often it is the last sentence.

> ### Types of Claims
>
> Most claims serve one of the following purposes:
>
> - clarify a definition
> - explain a cause or effect
> - make a judgment
> - advocate an action

Activity 1A Identifying Claims

Imagine your school is debating whether to allow students to bring their own e-book readers and tablets to school. Underline the claim in this paragraph and explain why you selected it.

> Students should be allowed to bring and use their own iPads, e-book readers, and laptops at school. The main reason this is a good idea is that technology enhances learning. Students would have greater access to information for research projects and would be able to incorporate digital elements into their writing and speaking projects. Studies have shown that students with access to laptops at school significantly outscore a control group in the areas of mathematics and language arts. There are so many advantages to allowing students to bring their own technology to school.

_____

_____

_____

_____

Activity 1B Evaluating Claims

Evaluate the following claims by writing "Yes" or "No" in Is it debatable? and Is it precise? columns. In the Revision column, rewrite the claim to make it better, or write "good" if no change is needed.

Claim	Is it debatable?	Is it precise?	Revision
1. Every school in America should be protected by three or more armed police officers.			
2. Physical education shouldn't be a required class.			
3. Our school has a dress code.			

Activity 1C Identifying Claims for Argument

In each row below, compare the statements in the first and second columns. Then explain why the statement in the Better Claim column is more effective as a claim for an argumentative essay.

Weak Claim	Better Claim	Explanation
1. Abraham Lincoln was a great president.	Because he freed the slaves and kept the United States from splitting into two separate countries, Abraham Lincoln was America's greatest president.	
2. I think that *The Hunger Games* trilogy is better than the Harry Potter series.	Students can relate more to the problems faced by Katniss in *The Hunger Games* than those faced by Harry in the Harry Potter series.	
3. Kids like to eat sugar.	Parents should limit the amount of sugar their children eat.	

Activity 1D Writing a Claim

Below is an excerpt from a government report on traumatic brain injuries. Read the passage and then write a claim that you can support using this passage.

Take Concussions Out of Play: Learn to Prevent, Recognize, and Respond to Concussions

The Center for Disease Control estimates 173,285 sports- and recreation-related traumatic brain injuries (TBIs), including concussions, among children and adolescents are treated in U.S. emergency departments each year.

A bump, blow, or jolt to the head can cause a concussion, a type of TBI. Concussions can also occur from a blow to the body that causes the head to move rapidly back and forth. Even a "ding," "getting your bell rung," or what seems to be a mild bump or blow to the head can be serious.

Concussions can occur in any sport or recreation activity. So, all coaches, parents, and athletes need to learn concussion signs and symptoms and what to do if a concussion occurs.

Source: <cdc.gov>

_____

_____

_____

_____

_____

_____

_____

_____

_____

Feedback on a Claim

For class assignments, ask a friend to read your claim and tell you whether people might disagree with it. On a test, imagine how a friend might respond to your claim.

LESSON 2 SUPPORT FOR CLAIMS

To win your readers to your point of view, you need to support your claim as strongly as you can. Most support is one of two kinds:

- **Evidence** includes facts and informed judgments.
- **Reasons** include logical conclusions from evidence or ideas.

> **Strength of Support**
>
> Support is strong if it comes from a reliable source and is stated precisely. In general, more recent information is stronger than older information.

 ## Activity 2A *Identifying Strong Support*

Each box includes a pair of similar sentences that might be used in an essay about year-round school. In each pair, underline the words that differ. In the Explanation box, explain why one sentence provides stronger support for a claim than the other one does.

A. According to a University of Missouri study, student test scores decline after summer vacation.	B. After summer vacation, I don't remember half of what I learned the previous year.
1. Explanation	

C. According to a survey conducted in 1990, a majority of parents would prefer a year-round school schedule.	D. A 2012 survey indicates that fifty-five percent of parents with elementary school students would prefer a school schedule with shorter breaks placed throughout the year.
2. Explanation	

E. I learn a lot from traveling with my family during the summer and going to summer camp, but not all families can afford to travel.	F. Families with higher incomes send their kids to summer camps and tutoring programs, but children in poorer families often spend summer break in front of the television.
3. Explanation	

Activity 2B Identifying Support for Claims

Read the following passage and follow the directions below it.

Bullying: Up Front and Virtual

Between 2001 and 2007, bullying has been on the rise and, in 2009, one in five high school students report that they were bullied on school property in the past year. Approximately eight percent of high school students admit to having bullied others, and about 6.5 percent of high schoolers are both bullies and victims of bullying. The risk of cyberbullying has also increased along with the growth of technology in the lives of adolescents . . . adolescents are most commonly cyberbullied via text message. In 2010, one in five adolescents said that they had been cyberbullied at some point in their lives, and about the same number admit to having been a cyberbully. One in ten adolescents had been both a cyberbully and a victim.

Source: <hhs.gov>

Analyzing Support

As you gather information to support your claim, think about how facts support or oppose your claim.

1. Underline a phrase or sentence in the text that supports this claim:

   "Our school should adopt an anti-bullying program."

2. Place a box around a phrase or sentence in the text that supports this claim:

   "Kids who are bullied often are bullies themselves."

LESSON 3 COUNTERCLAIMS

In your argumentative essay, you should present a **counterclaim,** or a statement that disagrees with your claim. For example, if you claim that soccer players are better all-around athletes than football players, possible counterclaims include the following:

- Both football players and soccer players are good athletes.
- Football players are better all-around athletes than soccer players.

In an argumentative essay, you should recognize the counterclaims of those who disagree with you and give some strong evidence for the counterclaim. Then you should respond to the counterclaim, giving arguments against it.

Activity 3A Writing Counterclaims

For each claim listed below, write a counterclaim.

Claim	Counterclaim
1. All students should be required to spend 20 hours volunteering in the community in order to pass 8th grade.	
2. Band or choir should be required for all 8th grade students.	
3. Students who play on a school athletic team should not be required to take physical education classes.	

Activity 3B Responding to Counterclaims

In the following paragraph, the claim is stated in the first sentence. Underline the counterclaim and the evidence supporting it. Circle the response to the evidence supporting the counterclaim.

> Our school should offer physical education classes for girls only and boys only. Some people would say that same-sex classes are discriminatory. They say that separating girls and boys will be returning to the past when girls were not allowed to play sports. However, forcing young women to play against boys is just as limiting. The solution is to offer both same-sex and single-sex classes so that everyone can be successful at his or her own level.

LESSON 4 EVIDENCE FROM SOURCES

Your writing should be based on evidence that you get from sources. On some tests, you may be provided with the sources to use. To prepare to use these sources, the test may ask you questions about the source, such as explaining vocabulary used in it, identifying its main idea, and writing a summary of it.

The following set of activities asks questions about a source that provides evidence you could use to write an essay in support of or in opposition to girls-only or boys-only classes.

Activity 4A Understanding Vocabulary

Read the following text. Annotate the text by underlining key ideas. Then answer the questions that follow.

> **Source 1**
>
> **Judge Stops West Virginia Single-Sex Classes: Were They a Success or Pseudoscience?**
> by Stacy Teicher Khadaroo
>
> *The following article is about separate classes for girls and boys at Van Devender Middle School in Parkersburg, West Virginia.*
>
> Van Devender started its single-sex classes in reading, math, social studies, and science for sixth-graders in 2010. The single-sex approach expanded to seventh-grade last year and eighth-grade this year.
>
> By the end of seventh-grade, students who were in single-sex classes for two years made larger gains on state tests than peers at coed middle schools, [Director of Secondary Education] Mr. Winland says. Teachers and students both noticed more focus in the classroom, because there was less posturing to impress the opposite sex.
>
> Such outcomes are often touted by Leonard Sax, a speaker and consultant who trains teachers based in part on the idea that brain-science suggests there are physiological differences between boys and girls.
>
> Mr. Sax visited a school in Dallas recently, for example, where low-income minority boys working in competitive teams were so motivated that they demanded more books so they could earn

continued on next page

continued from previous page

extra credit. An equivalent school for girls is also doing well, says Sax, founder and executive director of the National Association for Single-Sex Public Education.

Source: <abcnews.go.com>

Part A

Circle the letter before the choice that best explains what the word posturing means as it is used in this sentence from the text: "Teachers and students both noticed more focus in the classroom, because there was less posturing to impress the opposite sex."

    a. talking

    b. studying

    c. pretending

    d. fighting

Part B

Circle the letter before the choice that best helps the reader figure out the meaning of "posturing" as used in the text.

    a. focus

    b. classroom

    c. impress

    d. opposite sex

Internet Research

If a source makes references you don't recognize, use a search engine to look them up. For example, an Internet search would provide you with more information about Leonard Sax and the National Association for Single-Sex Public Education.

Vocabulary

A set of "selected response" questions can help you understand what you have just read. Some tests present them in two parts. The first might ask a question about your understanding of the text. The second might ask you to identify the evidence that supports your answer in the first part.

Activity 4B Identifying the Key Idea

Answer the following questions about the key idea of the excerpt from "Judge Stops West Virginia Single-Sex Classes: Were They a Success or Pseudoscience?"

Part A

Circle the letter before the choice that best states the main idea of the excerpt.

   a. Educators at Van Devender Middle School believe same-sex classes have improved student success.

   b. At a school in Dallas, boys are motivated by competition.

   c. A judge declared that same-sex classes in West Virginia are illegal.

   d. Science suggests there are physiological differences between boys' and girls' brains.

> **Key Idea**
> ....
> The first of a pair of questions might ask you to identify the key idea in a text. A second question might ask you to identify one or more statements that provide evidence for your choice.

Part B

Circle the letters before three pieces of evidence that support your answer to Part A.

   a. "Van Devender started its single-sex classes in reading, math, social studies, and science for sixth-graders in 2010."

   b. "By the end of seventh-grade, students who were in single-classes for two years made larger gains on state tests than peers at coed middle schools, [Director of Secondary Education] Mr. Winland says."

   c. "Teachers and students both noticed more focus in the classroom, because there was less posturing to impress the opposite sex."

   d. "Mr. Sax visited a school in Dallas recently, for example, where low-income minority boys working in competitive teams were so motivated that they demanded more books so they could earn extra credit."

   e. "An equivalent school for girls is also doing well, says Sax, founder and executive director of the National Association for Single-Sex Public Education."

LESSON 5

HOW TO WRITE AN ARGUMENTATIVE ESSAY

Below is a second source about same-sex classes. Following it is a model demonstrating the steps in writing an argumentative essay. Use these steps to help you write your own essays.

> ### Source 2
> ### The ACLU Challenges the Legality of Single-Sex Classes
>
> The American Civil Liberties Union [ACLU] is cracking down on schools that offer single-sex classes. Recently the ACLU sent letters to Florida and several other states asking them to investigate the legality of same-sex classes. The move was part of an initiative by the ACLU called "Teach Kids, Not Stereotypes." The ACLU has already temporarily stopped a West Virginia school district from offering single-gender classes until a lawsuit challenging the legality of single-sex programs is heard.
>
> Mie Lewis, a senior staff attorney with the ACLU, says that the emphasis on single-sex classes is based on bad science. "There's lots of kinds of new pseudoscience about the supposed brain differences in girls and boys," Lewis says, "It's age-old stereotypes that have been dressed up in the guise of neuroscience."
>
> Lewis supports the ACLU's position by pointing to a September 2011 article by former president of the American Psychological Association Diane F. Halperon, "The Pseudoscience of Single-Sex Schooling." In the article Halperon argues that single-sex classes "legitimize institutional sexism."
>
> Source: The above text is a summary of information found in "Palm Beach County Schools Experiment with Single-gender Classes to Boost Student Performance," by Allison Ross. <palmbeachpost.com>

Using Multiple Sources

When writing an argumentative essay for a test or other assignment, you might be asked to read several sources on the same topic. These additional sources will provide more evidence to use in your essay.

Step 1. Understand the prompt.

The directions for writing an essay are called the **prompt.** The verbs in it tell you what to do. Here is an example of a prompt:

> You have read two texts by two writers commenting on same-sex classes. Decide upon a claim you would like to make about all-boy or all-girl classes. Your claim may be in favor of same-sex classes or against same-sex classes. Use evidence such as quotations, facts, and reasons from the sources to support your claim. Include and respond to one counterclaim in your essay.

Activity 5A Analyzing the Prompt

In the prompt on page 24, underline up to 20 key words that tell you what to do. Then, rewrite the prompt in your own words.

_____

_____

_____

_____

_____

_____

Collaborate About Prompts

After you write your prompt, trade it with a partner. Discuss any differences in how you interpreted the prompt.

Step 2. Take notes on the sources.

You may have already analyzed the sources, but now you should take notes on them with the prompt in mind. Look for specific statements that you can use in your essay. If you use a graphic organizer, choose one that fits the directions stated in the prompt. See the table below for some ideas. After taking notes, you should state the claim you want to defend and include at least one counterclaim.

Words in the Prompt	Type of Graphic Organizer	Model
compare, contrast, distinguish	Venn diagram	
identify causes, explain effects	flowchart	
summarize, describe	web diagram	
evaluate, judge, weigh	two-column chart	

Activity 5B Analyzing Sources

The chart below includes notes from the two sources about same-sex classes shown on previous pages.

1. In the row for Academic Progress, underline the words that indicate whether the information came from the first or the second source.

2. Fill in one of the empty cells in the Gender Stereotypes row.

3. Fill in one of the empty cells in the Legality row.

4. In the final row of the chart, write a counterclaim.

Web Site Reliability

Many Web sites include an "About" tab that provides background on the person or organization that produces the site. This information can help you evaluate the reliability of information on the site.

Issue	Support for Same-Sex Classes	Support for Coed Classes
Academic Progress (Does it help students learn better?)	By the end of seventh-grade, students who were in single-sex classes for two years made larger gains on state tests than peers at coed middle schools, [Director of Secondary Education] Mr. Winland says (Khadaroo).	Lewis pointed to a September 2011 article by Diane F. Halpern, a former president of the American Psychological Association, called "The Pseudoscience of Single-Sex Schooling," that argues there's no well-designed research showing that same-sex classes work (Ross).
Discipline (Does it help with discipline problems?)	Teachers and students both noticed more focus in the classroom, because there was less posturing to impress the opposite sex (Khadaroo).	
Gender Stereotypes (Does it promote stereotypes?)		
Legality (Is it legal?)		
My Claim: Schools should allow same-sex classes.		
A Counterclaim:		

Step 3. Organize your ideas.

Use an outline to organize the ideas for your essay. Like most texts, an argumentative essay should include an introduction, body, and conclusion.

The **introduction** is the first paragraph of an essay. It should identify the topic and state the claim.

The **body** is the main part of an essay. In the body, present support for your claim—and remember that support includes both reasons and evidence. The body should also explain one counterclaim and a response to it. Here is a basic outline to help you organize the body of your essay.

> **Strong Opening**
>
> In the first line of the introduction, try using an interesting quotation or description of a controversial situation.

Basic Outline for the Body of an Argumentative Essay	
Paragraph 1	Reason 1 with support
Paragraph 2	Reason 2 with support
Paragraph 3	Counterclaim and response
Paragraph 4	Reason 3 (strongest reason) with support

The strengths of using this order include:

- the reader is immediately given convincing reasons and evidence before being given a counterclaim.

- the essay ends with the strongest reason, leaving the most convincing evidence in the reader's mind.

> **Strong Ending**
>
> Often, the last line of the conclusion is a short or dramatic sentence that will stick in the minds of readers.

The **conclusion** is the last paragraph of an essay. It should either summarize the main support for the claim or state the strongest support for the claim. It should always restate the claim.

Activity 5C Analyzing an Outline

On the following page is an outline for an argumentative essay about same-sex classrooms. As you read it, mark it as follows:

1. Circle the headers for each of the three main parts of the outline.

2. Underline the two places where the claim is mentioned.

3. Write *counterclaim* next to where the counterclaim is included in the outline.

4. Circle the transitional word that indicates that evidence is being presented against a counterclaim.

Sample Outline: Single-sex Classes

Claim: Schools should allow some same-sex classes.

I. Introduction
A. Van Devender Middle School in Parkersburg, West Virginia, has found success by offering classes that are for boys only or for girls only.
B. Schools should allow same-sex classes.

II. Body
A. Teachers notice a decrease in discipline problems.
B. During junior high, students feel more comfortable learning with students of the same sex.
C. Some groups say that single-sex classes are illegal because they promote stereotypes.
D. However, students should have the right to learn in an environment where they are comfortable.
E. Student test scores increase when students are placed in same-sex classes.

III. Conclusion
A. Same-sex classes help students learn better.
B. For certain subjects, students should be able to choose an all-boy or all-girl class if they want to.

Step 4. Write the draft.

Using your notes and your outline, write your essay.

 Activity 5D Analyzing Organization

On the next page is the draft of an essay about single-sex classes based upon the sources from previous pages along with other sources. As you read, mark it as indicated below. The draft includes some errors that you will be asked to correct in the next activity.

1. Write a note in the margin to identify the introduction.

2. Underline the claim in the introduction.

3. Indicate the reasons by writing *Reason 1, Reason 2,* and *Reason 3* in the margin.

4. Double underline the counterclaim.

5. Write a note in the margin to identify the conclusion.

Spell-Check

Spell-Checker is a handy tool to use when writing an essay on a computer. However, remember that spell-checker does not indicate when a correctly spelled word is used incorrectly. For example, imagine you type *Its over hear*, instead of *It's over here*. Spell-checker will miss both of these errors.

Sample Draft: In Support of Single-Sex Classes

At Van Devender Middle School in Parkersburg, West Virginia, something is missing from several classes. It's not books or desks or even teachers. It's boys. Several core classes contain only girls. The boys have their own math and reading classes—without any girls. Many other schools around the country are also discovering that same-sex classes are good. Clearly, schools should allow same-sex classes.

Benefits of Single-Sex Classes

First, teachers noticed a decrease in discipline problems. At Van Devender, teachers noticed that students were more focused in the classroom because boys and girls weren't trying to impress each other, but instead they could focus on learning (Khadaroo). Schools in South Carolina reported that 7 out of 10 schools with single-sex classes had a lower number of discipline issues than schools with coed classes (Chadwell).

Also, during middle school, students feel more comfortable learning with students of the same sex. I'm a junior high student and I think I would learn better in a classroom of all girls. Boys are just more immature than girls.

Legality Problems

Unfortunately some groups say that single-sex classes are illegal because they promote stereotypes. The American Civil Liberties Union has filed lawsuits against Van Devender Middle School and other schools with single-sex classes. These groups say that single-sex classrooms are based on stereotypes about how boys and girls learn. They believe that single-sex classrooms will teach kids that girls and boys are more different than alike (Ross).

This problem can be solved by having some classes that are not single-sex only. This way boys and girls can be together for part of the school day. However, students should have the right to learn in an environment where they are comfortable and where they don't have distractions. For important classes such as math and reading students should have the option of being in a class of all boys or all girls.

The most convincing reason for having single-sex

continued on next page

Formal Style

Some types of writing require you to use a more formal style. When writing in formal style, avoid using personal pronouns such as *I, we,* and *you*. Opinions are not as convincing as solid evidence. Which of the following sentences has more authority?

- I think that single-sex classes are a good idea.
- Research by schools around the world shows that single-sex classes are very effective.

Transitional Phrases

Notice how the writer uses transitional phrases as signals to guide the reader through the ideas presented in the essay. For example, the word *unfortunately* indicates that the writer is sharing something he or she believes is a bad idea—a counterclaim. Other transitional phrases that indicate a contrasting idea include *however, on the other hand,* and *in contrast*.

continued from previous page

classes is that students' test scores increase when placed in same-sex classes. Students at Van Devender Middle School, who were in single-sex classes, did better on state tests than students at coed middle schools (Khadaroo). Most of the all-boy and all-girl classes in South Carolina outperformed their peers in coed classes (Chadwell).

Schools should offer same-sex classes in important subjects such as reading and math. This will reduce discipline problems. Students will feel more comfortable in the class and will learn more. Having single-sex classes is a good idea and will help students learn more.

In-Text Citations

Notice that the writer uses the author's name in parentheses to indicate the source of the information. For more on in-text citations, see pages 55–56.

Step 5. Revise your essay.

After you write a draft, read it again carefully. First think about the content and development of your claim. Does each paragraph contain enough evidence and reasons to be convincing? Then think about your organization and writing style. Does the order make sense? Is the writing clear?

Issues to Check

As you write essays for class assignments, keep a list of specific issues that give you difficulty. Check these issues when you edit your essay.

Activity 5E Revising for Content

Analyze the following paragraph from the student model by answering the questions that follow.

Also, during middle school, students feel more comfortable learning with students of the same sex. I'm a junior high student and I think I would learn better in a classroom of all girls. Boys are just more immature than girls.

1. Does the first sentence contain a valid reason? If not, rewrite the reason on the lines below.

_____

_____

_____

_____

_____

2. Is enough evidence offered to support the reason in the paragraph? What types of information could be added to the paragraph so that the argument has more authority?

_____

_____

_____

_____

3. Should the third sentence be included or omitted? Why?

_____

_____

_____

Based upon your answers to the questions above, rewrite the paragraph from the previous page on the lines below. Use the following information to strengthen the argument.

Every year, we [the South Carolina Department of Education] administer student, parent, and teacher surveys at schools with single-gender classes with regard to self-confidence, motivation, participation, and desire to complete hard work. Last year's results [for the 2009 to 2010 school year] show that an average of 60 percent of the students' self-reports indicate that these characteristics increase by being in single-gender classes. ("New Voices" by David Chadwell at www.ascd.org)

Collaboration for Revision

Ask a partner to read your paragraph and rate the strength of your argument. Did your revision make your argument more convincing?

_____

_____

_____

_____

_____

_____

_____

_____

Activity 5F Rewriting a Paragraph

Reread the following excerpt from the essay and mark it up in the following ways:

1. Underline two places where the same subject and verb are used.

2. Place a box around a sentence that is too long and wordy.

First, teachers noticed a decrease in discipline problems. At Van Devender, teachers noticed that students were more focused in the classroom because boys and girls weren't trying to impress each other, but instead they could focus on learning (Khadaroo).

A couple of simple changes will greatly improve the writing in this paragraph. Good writing uses a variety of concise words. You can avoid redundancy by replacing repeated words with synonyms.

Redundant: Each and every day teachers teach subjects to students who don't want to learn.

Clear and concise: Every day teachers must instruct unmotivated students.

In the second sentence of the student model paragraph above, too many ideas are crammed into one long sentence. Consider fixing this sentence by dividing it into shorter sentences. Keep similar ideas together in one sentence. Place less important ideas in clauses or phrases.

Rewrite the paragraph from the student model, fixing the errors with repetitive verbs and the overly long second sentence.

_____

_____

_____

_____

_____

_____

_____

_____

_____

> ### Sentence Types
>
> Good writers use a variety of sentence types and lengths. One way to add sentence variety is to use a verbal, or a word that looks like a verb, but acts like another part of speech. Study the following examples of verbals:
>
> Gerund (noun): <u>Creating classes of all girls or all boys</u> is one way schools are trying to help students learn.
>
> Participle (adjective): <u>Looking to boost test scores</u>, schools are offering same-sex classes.
>
> Infinitive (adjective): Some schools are trying same-sex classes as a way <u>to help students learn better</u>.
>
> For more practice with verbals, see page 95.

> ### Collaboration on a Paragraph
>
> Ask a partner to read your paragraph and tell you whether it is clear and precise or unclear and redundant.

Step 6. Edit and proofread your essay.

You should follow norms and conventions regarding spelling, punctuation, grammar, and usage. Fix any errors you find and consider changes to make your text flow more smoothly.

One thing to check for when proofreading is correct usage of commas. Commas are used to

- Separate independent clauses when joined by *and, but, for, or, so, yet*

  Example: Wendy hated to cancel her party, but the weather was too bad.

- Set off introductory words or phrases

  Examples: If you can't get a ride, call me.

  Yes, I will be at school tomorrow.

- Set off words, phrases, and clauses in the middle of a sentence when they are not essential to the meaning of the sentence

  Examples: Next Friday, which happens to be my birthday, I will be flying to Florida for vacation.

  The best way to get to the highway, I believe, is to take Park Street.

- Set off items in a series

  Example: I will only eat macaroni and cheese, buttered toast, and saltine crackers.

Activity 5G Editing for Comma Usage

Correct the following sentences by adding or crossing out commas as needed.

1. I'm a junior high student and I think I would learn better in a classroom of all girls.

2. Unfortunately some groups say that single-sex classes are illegal because they promote stereotypes.

3. For important classes such as math and reading students should have the option of being in a class of all-boys, or all-girls.

4. Students at Van Devender Middle School, who were in single-sex classes, did better on state tests than students at coed middle schools.

LESSON 6 YOU TRY IT

Now it is your turn to write an argumentative essay. Use what you have learned in this chapter about claims, counterclaims, and evidence. Follow the steps outlined in the last lesson. They are also listed in the box on the right.

Steps in Writing an Argumentative Essay

1. Understand the prompt.
2. Take notes on the sources.
3. Organize your ideas.
4. Write the draft.
5. Revise your essay.
6. Edit and proofread your essay.

Activity 6A Writing an Argumentative Essay

Write an argumentative essay in response to one of the following prompts. Use information from at least three sources.

A. Limits on Screen Time	B. Gun Control
Imagine your parents are considering limiting the time you spend watching television, playing video games, and browsing the Internet to one hour during school days and two hours on the weekends. Conduct research and then state a position in support of or against these restrictions. Write an argumentative essay supporting your claim. Address one counterclaim. Support your ideas with relevant evidence from your research.	Due to recent school shootings, gun control advocates are proposing stricter gun control laws, including limiting both the types of guns that are legal and who can buy guns. Conduct research and then write a claim about whether more restrictions on guns should be made into law. Address one counterclaim and support your ideas with relevant evidence.

Checklist

Use the following checklist to edit and revise your essay.

My writing has . . .	
DEVELOPMENT	❏ a clear central claim ❏ strong supporting evidence ❏ a counterclaim, or opposing claim
ORGANIZATION	❏ a clear introduction, body, and conclusion ❏ good transitions ❏ logical order
EVIDENCE	❏ strong, relevant textual evidence ❏ enough evidence to be convincing
LANGUAGE & STYLE	❏ precise, appropriate word choice ❏ a formal, objective tone
GRAMMAR, SPELLING, & PUNCTUATION	❏ standard grammar ❏ correct spelling ❏ proper punctuation

Writing an Informative Essay

The purpose of an informative/explanatory essay is to explain or to provide information about a topic. When you explain the process of photosynthesis, describe the events leading up to World War I, or analyze the causes of global warming, you are using informative writing.

> **Informative Essays**
> - Increase the reader's knowledge of a subject
> - Help the reader understand a process or procedure

LESSON 1 THESIS STATEMENT

The purpose of your informative essay should be communicated in the main idea statement, also called the *thesis statement*. A **thesis statement** should clearly state the central idea of an essay. It should

- be clear and precise
- fulfill the requirements of the test prompt
- be based upon the texts you were asked to read

A good thesis statement should not begin with "My main idea is . . ." or "In this essay I will . . ."

Activity 1A *Making a Thesis Statement Precise*

Select the statement below that is most precise and label it good. *Rewrite the other two to make them more precise.*

Thesis Statement	Revision
1. I'm going to explain the results of global warming.	
2. The Constitution includes a series of checks and balances to limit the powers of the three branches of the federal government.	
3. It's easy to make homemade tortillas.	

Activity 1B *Writing a Thesis Statement*

Below is an excerpt from a timeline on women's suffrage. Read the facts and then write a strong thesis statement.

Timeline of Women's Suffrage

- 1848 First women's rights convention is held in Seneca Falls, NY.

- 1866 Elizabeth Cady Stanton and Susan B. Anthony form the American Equal Rights Association, dedicated to securing the right to vote for white women and African Americans.

- 1872 Susan B. Anthony is arrested and brought to trial in Rochester, New York, for attempting to vote for Ulysses S. Grant.

- 1878 Woman's suffrage amendment is introduced in Congress.

- 1916 Jeannette Rankin of Montana becomes the first American woman elected to Congress.

- 1920 The Nineteenth Amendment gives women the right to vote.

- 1923 The National Woman's party first proposes the Equal Rights Amendment to eliminate discrimination on the basis of gender. It has never been ratified.

Source: <memory.loc.gov>

AMENDMENT 19

(Ratified August 18, 1920)

The right of citizens of the United States to vote shall not be denied or abridged by the United States or by any State on account of sex.

Congress shall have the power to enforce this article by appropriate legislation.

AMENDMEN

January 23, 1

Thesis Statement:

_____

_____

_____

_____

LESSON 2 SUPPORT FOR THE THESIS STATEMENT

Your thesis statement should be developed with appropriate supporting details. These might include facts, examples, incidents, analogies, or causes and effects. Strong supporting details are relevant, or directly related, to the thesis statement.

Activity 2A *Evaluating Supporting Details*

Cross out sentences that would not convey good supporting details for the thesis statement. In the margin, write notes explaining why.

> **Thesis Statement: Due to budget cuts, many schools are cutting their fine arts programs.**
>
> **Possible Supporting Details**
>
> - Many middle and high schools with large numbers of poor students do not offer music.
> - The Secretary of Education said, "It is deeply troubling that all students do not have access to arts education today."
> - Last year our school performed the musical *Grease*.
> - Money that used to fund school bands and choirs is now being used for teachers' salaries for subjects such as math and science.
> - Art therapy can help children who have experienced abuse or traumatic events.
> - Some students are motivated to attend school because they love music, art, or drama.
> - The number of elementary schools offering drama classes declined from 20 percent to 4 percent in 2012.
> - It is unfair that sports programs are cut less often than music and art classes.

Activity 2B *Writing Supporting Details*

Write three good supporting details you might use to support this thesis statement: Junior high/Middle school is different from elementary school in several ways.

1. _____

_____

2. _____

_____

3. _____

_____

Maintaining Purpose

When choosing supporting details, remember the focus of informative writing is to convey ideas, not to persuade the reader to agree with your opinion.

LESSON 3 ANALYZING SOURCES

A writing test that asks you to write an informative essay may first ask you to read and answer questions about a passage or passages that you will use in writing your essay.

Activity 3A Writing a Summary

Read and annotate the following text. Write a summary statement on the lines below.

Source 1

The Pennsylvania Guide to Hydraulic Fracturing, or "Fracking"

Slick water hydraulic fracturing or "fracking" is a technology used to extract natural gas and oil that lies within a shale rock formation thousands of feet beneath the earth's surface.

Combined with another technique called "horizontal drilling," natural gas companies are able to drill previously untapped reserves. The combination of the two has resulted in a boom in domestic oil and gas production over the past five years. Horizontal drilling allows one surface well to tap gas trapped over hundreds of acres. Once the conventional vertical drill hits the shale formation, it turns horizontally. Drilling can then occur in several directions, much like the spokes of a wheel. The well is cased with steel and cement, which is meant to protect gas and frack water from leaking out. Explosives are placed at intervals along the horizontal section of the well to perforate the steel casing. These holes allow the gas, which is trapped in tight formations, to flow up the vertical section of the well. Under very high pressure, a combination of water, sand and chemicals is sent deep into the earth to create cracks and fissures in the shale rock. Those fissures are held open by the sand, allowing the natural gas to flow through those cracks, into the well bore and up to the surface.

Source:<stateimpact.npr.org>

_____

_____

_____

_____

_____

Activity 3B *Answering Questions About a Source*

Read and annotate the following text. Answer the questions that follow.

Source 2

"Fracking Fuels Energy Debate," by Erica Gies

Some researchers have begun linking fracking to groundwater pollution. To date, science has found conflicting results. But that's not the only concern. In recent months, other scientists have linked fracking to earthquakes.

At a meeting of the American Association for the Advancement of Science (or AAAS) in Vancouver, Canada, last February, scientists agreed there was a need for more research on fracking.

But a number of researchers now argue that the problem is not fracking—used to open up a gas reservoir—but instead the process of bringing that gas to the surface via wells. Indeed, much of the pollution being linked to gas production can occur up to a kilometer above where the fracking took place. That suggests that pollution associated with this gas comes from poor management of gas-production wells or of wastewater, says Charles Groat, a researcher at the University of Texas at Austin. His own team found similar results, which he presented at the AAAS meeting.

Given these findings, he said that focusing on fracking may distract people from making sure gas producers improve the seals on their wells' piping—the apparent main source of pollution.

Source: <sciencenews.org>

Part A *Which of the following sentences best summarizes the main idea of the passage?*

a. Scientists are concerned that fracking pollutes groundwater.

b. Fracking may cause earthquakes.

c. Researchers believe fracking negatively impacts the environment.

d. The main source of pollution comes from faulty seals on the wells' piping.

Part B *Choose two of the following sentences that could be used to support your answer to the question above.*

a. At a meeting of the American Association for the Advancement of Science (or AAAS) in Vancouver, Canada, last February, scientists agreed there was a need for more research on fracking.

b. And new studies are coming out regularly, helping environmental and energy engineers to better understand the impacts of fracking.

c. But a number of researchers now argue that the problem is not fracking . . . but instead the process of bringing that gas to the surface via wells.

d. Some researchers have begun linking fracking to groundwater pollution.

LESSON 4 HOW TO WRITE AN INFORMATIVE ESSAY

Following is a model demonstrating the steps in writing an informative essay. Use them to help you write your own essays.

Step 1. Understand the prompt.

The directions for writing an essay are called the **prompt.** The verbs in the prompt tell you what to do. Here is an example of a prompt:

> Because natural gas is a cleaner form of energy than oil and coal, energy producers are increasingly using hydraulic fracturing, or fracking, to extract natural gas out of shale rock. Write an essay explaining how the process of fracking works. Then explain some of the concerns environmental scientists have about the fracking process.

Activity 4A Analyzing the Prompt

In the prompt above, underline key words that tell you what to do. Write a purpose statement for your essay below.

My purpose is to: _____

_____

Step 2. Take notes on the sources.

You have already analyzed the sources, but now you should take notes on them with the prompt in mind. Go back to the texts you read. Look for specific statements that will fit with the purpose of your essay.

Activity 4B Gathering Ideas

Return to the sources found on pages 38–39. Look at the main ideas you underlined. On the lines below, write some key ideas you will want to include in your essay.

_____

_____

_____

_____

_____

_____

Writing an Essay

You can use the following eight steps to help you write an informative essay.

1. Understand the prompt.
2. Take notes on the sources.
3. Write a thesis statement.
4. Organize your ideas.
5. Develop a complete outline.
6. Write the draft.
7. Revise your essay.
8. Edit and proofread your essay.

Keeping Track of Information

Keep track of the sources of your information in your notes by jotting down the author's name (or title of the article) and page number after the note. You will need this information as you write your paper, and recording it with your notes will save time later.

Step 3. Write a thesis statement.

Once you've gathered some ideas that you want to include in your essay, you can write a thesis statement. Your thesis statement will be included in the introduction of your essay and will guide the ideas you include in the body of your paper.

Activity 4C Writing a Thesis Statement

Based upon your notes, write a thesis statement for your paper.

_____

_____

_____

_____

Step 4. Organize your ideas.

The next step is to figure out the best order in which to present your ideas. The order should be logical so that the reader can easily follow your train of thought.

You can use a graphic organizer or an outline to organize your ideas. If you use a graphic organizer to organize your main points, choose one that fits the directions stated in the prompt.

Words in the Prompt	Type of Graphic Organizer	Model
compare or contrast	Venn diagram	
cause or effect steps in a process	flowchart	
summarize	web diagram	

Activity 4D Creating a Graphic Organizer

Fill in the flowchart with information from your notes. Choose details based upon the thesis statement you wrote on the previous page.

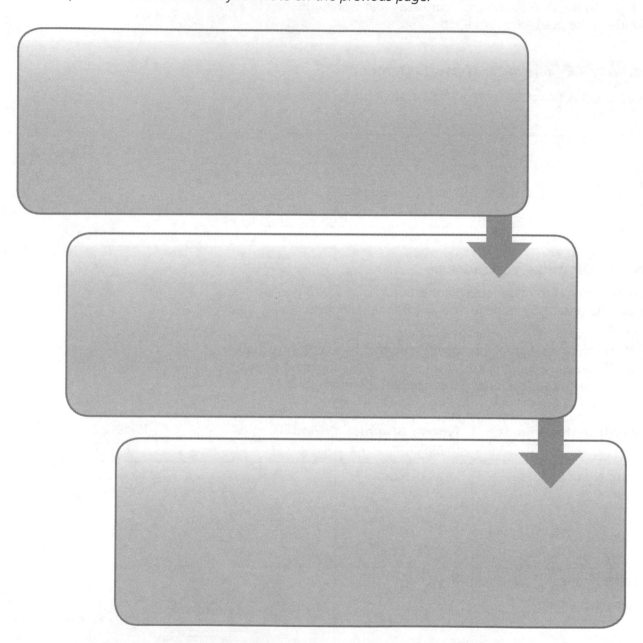

Step 5. Develop a complete outline.

An informative essay should include an introduction, a body, and a conclusion.

The **introduction** should introduce the topic and include the thesis statement.

The **body** should develop the thesis statement using supporting details.

The **conclusion** should restate the thesis statement. It should give a sense of closure to the writing.

Activity 4E Analyzing an Outline

Below is an outline that a student might have written before drafting an informative essay about fracking. As you read it, mark it as follows:

1. Circle the heading for each of the three main parts of the outline.

2. Underline the two places where the thesis statement is specifically mentioned.

3. Write the answer to this question in the margin of the outline: Why is the first paragraph of the body important?

4. Are the main points in the body in logical order? Why or why not?

_____

_____

_____

> **Defining Terms**
>
> When writing an informative essay on a topic related to science or other technical subjects, explaining unfamiliar vocabulary will help make a complex subject more manageable for both the writer and the reader.

Sample Outline:
Fracking: Energy Solution or Environmental Problem

I. Introduction
   A. Natural gas is a cleaner type of energy than gas and oil.
   B. Fracking is the process of drilling down into the earth to extract natural gas, but scientists are concerned that the process of getting this gas will hurt the environment.

II. Body
   A. A drill digs deep into the earth vertically and then horizontally.

   B. Explosives create holes in the piping for the gas to flow into.

   C. Water, sand, and chemicals are forced through the pipes into the earth, creating fissures in the shale rock.

   D. Natural gas flows out of the rock, into the pipe, and up to the surface.

III. Conclusion
   A. Although the goal of fracking is to find environmentally-friendly natural gas, the process of fracking may damage the environment.
   B. More research is needed in order to make fracking safer.

Step 6. Write the draft.

Using your notes and your outline, write your first draft.

 Activity 4F Analyzing a Draft

Below is the draft of an essay based on the prompt given. It contains some errors that you will correct in an activity that follows. As you read it, mark it as follows.

1. Write a note in the margin to identify the introduction and the conclusion.

2. Underline the thesis statement.

3. Place a check in the margin beside three specific pieces of evidence from the sources.

4. Circle three transitional phrases.

Sample Draft:
Fracking: Energy Solution or Environmental Problem

The United States is working hard to transition from using fossil fuels like coal and oil to using cleaner and renewable forms of energy. One cleaner type of fossil fuel is natural gas. New technology is making it easier to get to untaped sources of natural gas. Fracking is the process of drilling down into the earth to extract natural gas, but scientists are concerned that the process of getting this gas will hurt the environment.

Process of Fracking

Slick water hydraulic fracturing, or fracking, begins with a drill digging deep into the earth. First, the drill digs a vertical hole, and then, once it reaches shale rock, a horizontal tunnel is dug. A series of explosives create holes in the well's pipe, making holes for the gas to flow into ("Pennsylvania").

Next, water, sand, and chemicals are forced down the well. The mixture bursts out the holes in the pipe and create cracks in the shale rock. The sand keeps the cracks open and allows the natural gas to flow out of the rock into the pipe and up to the surface

Style and Tone

Writing assessments require a formal style. Avoid informal personal pronouns *(I, you)* and slang. Keep the tone objective; avoid giving your personal opinions.

Headings

Notice that headings are used to introduce the content in the body. Headings can aid the reader's comprehension, especially when you are writing about complex ideas.

continued on next page

continued from previous page

("Pennsylvania"). The gas is stored in tanks until it is piped out to homes around the country.

Scientists have some concerns about fracking. Some belive that the process contaminates the groundwater or causes earthquakes. But a number of researchers now argue that the problem is not fracking—used to open up a gas reservoir—but instead the process of bringing that gas to the surface via wells. One researcher, Charles Groat, indicated that since the polluted water is far away from where the fracking took place that means that the pollution associated with this gas comes from poor management of gas-production wells or of wastewater (Gies).

Although the goal of fracking is to find environmentally-friendly natural gas, the process of fracking may damage the environment. More research is needed in order to make fracking safer.

> **Citing Sources**
>
> This essay uses in-text citations to indicate the sources of information. With some writing assignments, you may be required to use in-text citations and to include a list of all your sources, or a works cited page. For more information on citing sources, see pages 55–56.

Step 7. Revise your essay.

After you write your first draft, read and evaluate it for problems with content and writing style. First think about each paragraph in your essay. Do any seem incomplete or underdeveloped? Reread the conclusion of the essay. Does it provide a satisfying ending?

Activity 4G Revising Content

Rewrite the model essay's conclusion by adding two more sentences to it. Go back and reread the sources on previous pages in order to find strong details you can add. Rewrite the conclusion on the following lines.

_____

_____

_____

_____

_____

_____

Activity 4H Rereading an Essay

Read the draft and answer these questions about possible revisions.

1. Does the essay define unfamiliar scientific terms? Give an example below. Identify any terms that could be explained better.

_____

_____

2. Which paragraph could benefit from a heading? Write a good header below.

_____

_____

3. What type of graphic or picture might help aid the reader's understanding of fracking?

_____

_____

4. In the fourth paragraph, find a sentence that is plagiarized from Source 2. Rewrite the sentence in your own words.

_____

_____

_____

_____

Step 8. Edit and proofread your essay.

After you finish revising the content and style of your essay, read through it carefully, correcting mistakes in grammar, spelling, and punctuation.

Consider the following sentence from the student model. What is different about the two underlined sections?

First, the <u>drill digs</u> a vertical hole and then, once it reaches the shale rock, <u>a horizontal tunnel is dug</u> by the drill.

The first underlined part uses an **active voice verb**. The drill is performing the digging. In the second underlined example, the tunnel is being acted upon by the drill. This is a **passive voice verb**. Here are more examples:

> ### Collaborate on Rereading Essays
>
> In a small group, discuss the strengths and weaknesses of the draft essay. For example, identify where the draft uses relevant facts, concrete details, and precise language. Also identify where the draft needs revision.

> ### Plagiarism
>
> Using someone else's ideas word for word in your essay is plagiarism. Plagiarism is a very serious matter. You can avoid it by using quotation marks around direct quotations or paraphrasing information in your own words.

Passive Voice: The ball <u>was thrown</u> by Lisa.
Active Voice: Lisa <u>threw</u> the ball.

Active voice verbs emphasize the person or thing doing the action. Passive voice verbs downplay the person or thing doing the action. Using active voice verbs makes your writing stronger. Use passive voice when you don't know who is doing the action. Avoid switching from active to passive voice in the middle of a sentence.

> **Incorrect:** I ate a piece of pie, and the ice cream was eaten by Sasha.
> **Correct:** I ate the piece of pie, and Sasha ate the ice cream.

From Passive to Active Voice

Sentences written in passive voice often contain a prepositional phrase beginning with *by*. To rewrite the sentence in active voice, make the word after *by* the subject.

Passive voice: The game was won by the Hawks.

Active voice: The Hawks won the game.

Activity 4I Using Active Voice Verbs

Rewrite the sentences so that verbs are in active voice.

1. First, the drill digs a vertical hole, and then, once it reaches the shale rock, a horizontal tunnel is dug by the drill.

_____

_____

2. The bill was passed by the Senate, and then the President signed it.

_____

_____

3. During the experiment, the chemical was diluted by the scientist.

_____

_____

Activity 4J Proofreading a Model Essay

Proofread the model essay by finding and correcting the following errors.

1. Correct two misspelled words.

2. Insert commas missing from a list of words.

3. Correct two verbs that do not agree with their subjects.

4. Fix one sentence fragment.

LESSON 5 YOU TRY IT

Activity 5A *Writing an Informative Essay*

Choose one of the following prompts and write an essay using the steps outlined in this chapter and listed below. Then use the checklist to make sure your writing conforms to the Characteristics of Good Writing.

A. Global Warming	B. Technology and Jobs
How is global warming impacting our Earth? What changes are scientists seeing in the environment? Conduct research and then write an informative essay explaining two or more impacts of global warming. Use evidence from sources in your writing.	Technology is changing the job market. Conduct research to find out how advances in technology are affecting the number and types of jobs available for American workers. Include textual evidence to support your main points.

Checklist

Use the following checklist to edit your essay.

My writing has . . .	
DEVELOPMENT	❏ a clear thesis statement ❏ strong supporting points ❏ relevant information based upon research
ORGANIZATION	❏ a clear introduction, body, and conclusion ❏ good transitions ❏ a logical order
EVIDENCE	❏ strong, relevant textual evidence ❏ direct quotations or paraphrased information from sources
LANGUAGE & STYLE	❏ precise, appropriate word choice ❏ a formal, objective tone
GRAMMAR, SPELLING, & PUNCTUATION	❏ standard grammar ❏ correct spelling ❏ proper punctuation

Steps for Writing an Informative Essay

1. Understand the prompt.
2. Take notes on the sources.
3. Write a thesis statement.
4. Organize your ideas.
5. Develop a complete outline.
6. Write the draft.
7. Revise your essay.
8. Edit and proofread your essay.

Reporting on Research

In a research report, you gather information from multiple sources to help you answer a question or solve a problem. This process of combining information from different sources into one report is called **synthesizing.**

LESSON 1 TOPICS FOR RESEARCH

The question or problem you research might be identified for you by your teacher or on a test. Or, you may be given a general subject and be asked to narrow the large subject down to a manageable topic. A good topic

- is broad enough that you can easily find multiple sources about it
- is narrow enough that you can cover it in the time you have available to research and write
- does not include bias or opinionated statements

The following are sample topics for a five-page research report:

Questions to Answer	Problems to Solve
How are immigrants and immigration policy today different from the early 1900s?	The government's use of enhanced interrogation in the fight against terrorism
How did industrialization transform America socially, politically, and economically?	The high dropout rate at your school

> **Fairness in Phrasing**
>
> A good question for research allows for more than one reasonable answer. "Why is math a waste of time?" is not a good question because it indicates that the writer already has a strong bias about the topic.

Activity 1A Phrasing a Research Question

Select the question that is phrased best for a research project. Then explain your choice.

A. Why does Hollywood insist on promoting gun violence in movies?

B. Which Hollywood director produces the most violent movies?

C. Do violent movies promote a culture of violence in America?

_____

_____

_____

_____

Activity 1B *Selecting a Question or Problem*

Below are some general subjects for a five-page research report. Underneath 1 and 2 are three possible questions or problems to address in the report. Place a check in the column to indicate which of the three is too broad, which is right in scope, and which is too narrow. Then under 3 write a good research question with the right scope for a five-page paper.

Question or Problem	Too Broad	Right Scope	Too Narrow
1. General Subject: Questions About Mental Illness			
A. How do doctors treat mental illness?			
B. Should mentally ill people who commit crimes be sent to prison?			
C. What are the symptoms of schizophrenia?			
2. General Subject: Questions About Offshore Oil Drilling			
A. Should offshore drilling be banned?			
B. How does offshore drilling affect the habitat of the bottlenose dolphin in the Gulf of Mexico?			
C. What is the history of offshore drilling?			
3. General Subject: The Problem of Bullying			
Good research question:			

LESSON 2 RELEVANT INFORMATION

In order to answer your research question, you need to find appropriate information from sources. Your sources may include online Web sites, books, videos, and interviews. Your sources should be **relevant** and **authoritative**.

- **Relevant sources** are ones that include information that is useful for your report.
- **Authoritative sources** are ones produced by knowledgeable experts in their field of study.

Activity 2A Identifying Relevant Sources

In the row under each category, circle the title of the source you think would be more useful for a research report on national efforts to stop childhood obesity. In the space at the end of each row, write a phrase that explains the advantage of the option you circled.

Source 1	Source 2	Explanation
1. Encyclopedia articles		
"Obesity"	"Weight loss"	
2. Web sites		
a site promoting exercise and healthy eating for children	a government-run site explaining the health effects of childhood obesity	
3. Books		
Preventing Childhood Obesity, a nonfiction book	*Skinny,* a novel about a teenager who weighs over 300 pounds	
4. News articles		
"Solving the Childhood Obesity Puzzle" in a medical journal	"Is Your Child Too Fat?: Spotting the Signs of Obesity" in a women's magazine	

Activity 2B Evaluating Reliability

Rate the reliability of each source on the subject of the health effects of childhood obesity. Use a scale of 1, not reliable, to 5, very reliable. Then review your answers and write a description of what makes a source reliable.

_____ A. A doctor who treats overweight children

_____ B. A weight-loss coach

_____ C. A researcher who studies obesity

_____ D. A blogger who writes about health issues

_____ E. A biography by a woman who was obese as a child

_____ F. A television reality show about people trying to lose weight

_____ G. An overweight ten-year-old

What makes a source reliable?

_____

_____

_____

Collaborate to Evaluate Reliability

How reliable a person considers a source about a controversial topic might reflect on that person's point of view. If you are uncertain whether to use a source, discuss it with people who do not share your viewpoint.

As you read your sources, you should underline main ideas and information you want to include in your essay. This is called *annotating a text*. **Annotate** a text by

- underlining important points
- writing questions
- making notes in the margins

If you are not able to write in a text, take notes on another piece of paper or in a computer file. Be sure to keep track of which source the information came from.

Activity 2C Annotating Sources

Read and annotate the following source. Then answer the questions that follow.

Source 1

The nation's growing recognition of the obesity crisis as a major public heath concern for our children and youth has led to an array of diverse efforts aimed at increasing physical activity and promoting healthful eating. These efforts, however, generally remain fragmented

---

continued on next page

continued from previous page

and small-scale. Furthermore, there is a lack of systematic tracking and evaluation of childhood obesity prevention interventions. When compared to the strong commitment and heavy infusion of governmental and private-sector resources devoted to other possible major public health concerns, such as infectious disease outbreaks or bioterrorism events, there is a marked underinvestment in the prevention of childhood obesity and related chronic diseases.

Addressing the childhood obesity epidemic is a collective responsibility involving multiple stakeholders and different sectors—including the federal government, state and local governments, communities, schools, industry, media, and families.

Source: *Progress in Preventing Childhood Obesity: How Do We Measure Up?* Institute of Medicine of the National Academies. page 1

Part A

Circle the letter before the sentence that best expresses the writer's key idea about obesity.

a. Obesity can be stopped by more healthy eating habits and increased physical activity.

b. The nation has invested much time trying to stop infectious diseases and bioterrorism.

c. Childhood obesity is an important problem which has not received enough attention.

d. Schools should increase physical activity for students during the school day.

Two-Part Questions

Tests may include questions about vocabulary or key ideas followed by a question that asks you to identify the evidence for the answer you provided. These questions may be labeled Part A and Part B.

Part B

Circle the letters before the two statements that provide the most direct evidence for the writer's key idea about childhood obesity.

a. "The nation's growing recognition of the obesity crisis as a major public heath concern . . ."

b. "increasing physical activity and promoting healthful eating"

c. "These efforts, however, generally remain fragmented and small-scale . . ."

d. ". . . there is a marked underinvestment in the prevention of childhood obesity and related chronic diseases."

LESSON 3 TAKING NOTES FROM SOURCES

After reading your sources, take accurate notes, recording important ideas you want to use in your paper. You may record your notes in a notebook, on notecards, or in a computer file. Three basic types of note-taking include:

Summary

Condense a longer passage into a shortened version. Use your own words.

> One out of three kids in the United States is obese. Overweight children are likely to become obese adults plagued by diabetes and heart disease. At the current rate, half of all Americans will be obese by 2030. (Haupt)

Paraphrase

Restate information in your own words.

> If the current childhood obesity rates don't change, half of all Americans will be obese by 2030. (Haupt)

As you take notes, be sure to record the source of the note. Instead of recording the entire title, write the author's last name and the page number, if there is one. If no author is given, record the title or a key word from the title with the page number. ("Solving Obesity Puzzle" 19). You will learn more on this in Lesson 4.

Quotation

Record a statement word for word from a source using quotation marks. This will help you avoid plagiarism, or taking credit for something someone else wrote.

> "One in three kids in the United States is obese, and another third is overweight." (Haupt)

Activity 3A Taking Notes

Take two notes—one a quotation and the other a paraphrase—from the source in Activity 2C on pp. 52–53. Record the source information at the end of each note.

Quotation:

_____

_____

_____

Paraphrase:

_____

_____

_____

> **To Summarize, to Paraphrase, or to Quote?**
>
> Summarize a source if it has good general ideas, but few useful details.
>
> Paraphrase a source if it has good details, but the specific words used are not that important. Most of your notes should be paraphrases.
>
> Quote a source when the language is effective or memorable or you can't say it better yourself. Use quotations sparingly.

LESSON 4 CITATIONS AND QUOTATIONS

When writing a research report, you must give credit to your sources within the paper itself. This is why it is important to keep track of where your notes come from (see Lesson 3). If you don't credit your sources in your paper, the reader will assume that the ideas are yours. Presenting someone else's ideas as your own is called **plagiarism**. Many schools have severe penalties for plagiarism. You can avoid plagiarism if you use

- in-text citations to give credit to your sources
- quotation marks when you use another writer's exact words
- a list of all the sources used in your paper—a works cited page

Citations

A **citation** is a note included in your report that identifies the source of information. In one commonly used format for citations (MLA):

- The standard format is to include the author's last name and page number where the information can be found. (Gonzales 23) If no page number is given, just include the author's name. (Gonzales)

- If the work doesn't have an author, use a key word or words from the title of the book (in italics) or article (in quotation marks). Also include the page number, if available. ("Overweight" 16)

Here is an example of an in-text citation of paraphrased information:

> In 1860 and 1861, as slave states left the Union, many antislavery leaders preferred to let them go rather than to start a war to stop them (Foner 146).

The citation indicates that the information in the sentence came from page 146 of a book by an author named Foner. The author's full name (Eric Foner), the book title *(The Fiery Trial),* and other information about the book should appear in a list of sources at the end of a report called the Works Cited page. Notice that the period for the sentence goes after the in-text citation.

Quotations

If you repeat a statement word for word from a source, enclose the words in quotation marks. If you use information from a source but phrase it in your own words, do not use quotation marks.

Here is an example of a quotation:

> Abraham Lincoln once told a supporter, "I must, in candor, say I do not think myself fit for the Presidency" (Foner 135).

Citations on Tests

Citations may not be required for essays on tests. However, including them is a good habit. By indicating your sources, you can easily go back to them if you need to.

Citations with Page Numbers Only

If you have already mentioned the name of the author in your writing, you only need to put the page number in your citation. Here is an example:

Historian Eric Foner says that many antislavery leaders preferred to let slave states leave the Union rather than to start a war to stop them (146).

Works Cited

A works cited page is a list of all the sources used in your paper, written in the following general format:

Last name, First name. Title of work. City of Publisher: Publisher, Year of Publication. Medium of Publication.

Below are some examples of works cited entries. Consult your teacher for his or her preferred styles.

Listing for an online government report:

Frieden, Thomas R. *Preventing Tobacco Use Among Youth and Young Adults.* Office of the Surgeon General, 2012. Web. 22 Oct. 2012.

A Web page:

"Teen Smoking: 10 Ways to Keep Teens Smoke-free." *www. mayoclinic.com.* The Mayo Clinic, Nov. 10, 2012. Web. 31 January 2013.

Activity 4A *Using Citations and Quotations*

The excerpt below is from the Robert Wood Johnson Foundation Web site (www.rwjf.org) under the title "Childhood Obesity: Marketing to Kids." No date was given. Follow the directions below.

> Unhealthy foods and beverages are heavily marketed to children, and research shows that exposure to food marketing messages increases children's obesity risk. Food and beverage companies also target African-American and Latino children with more advertising and for products that are less healthy.

1. Write a sentence that uses a direct quotation from the excerpt. Use an in-text citation to give credit to the source.

_____

_____

_____

_____

2. Write a works cited entry for this source.

_____

> ### Dates and Web sites
>
> Note that works cited entries for Web sites contain two dates. The first is the date the page or online article was written or updated. The final date is the day the writer accessed the page.

LESSON 5 HOW TO WRITE A RESEARCH REPORT

Following is a model demonstrating the six steps in writing a research report. Use these six steps to help you write your own reports.

Step 1. Understand the prompt.

Begin by reading the directions closely. The directions that explain what to write about are called a **prompt.**

- The prompt might describe a general topic, such as school discipline codes. You will need to narrow the subject down to a topic you can cover in your report.

- The prompt might already be very well defined. It may come either before or after the sources that will provide the textual evidence you will use in your report.

Activity 5A Analyzing the Prompt

Underline key words and phrases in the following prompt.

> Recent research indicates that childhood obesity is a major problem in the United States. Describe the problem and explain what measures are being taken to combat the problem.

Now write some questions that will guide your research. One example has been done for you.

> How big of a problem is obesity? How many children are obese?

_____

_____

_____

_____

_____

_____

Step 2. Take notes on the sources.

Whether the sources are provided for you on a test or you find your own, take notes on them with your purpose in mind.

- Annotate or underline main ideas as you read the sources.

- To help you find the notes later, write a brief note in the margin identifying the main idea of the underlined text.

Interpreting the Prompt

Many students score poorly on writing tests because they do not read the prompt carefully enough. For example, think of the difference between a prompt that asks you to *describe* your school and one that asks you to *evaluate* your school.

Annotating Sources

To understand how to annotate a text, see page 52.

Activity 5B Annotating Sources

Read and annotate the following sources. An example is done for you.

Source 2

"Childhood Obesity Facts"

- Childhood obesity has more than doubled in children and tripled in adolescents in the past 30 years.

  Shows how big the problem is

- The percentage of children aged 6–11 years in the United States who were obese increased from 7% in 1980 to nearly 18% in 2010. Similarly, the percentage of adolescents aged 12–19 years who were obese increased from 5% to 18% over the same period.

- In 2010, more than one-third of children and adolescents were overweight or obese.

- Overweight is defined as having excess body weight for a particular height from fat, muscle, bone, water, or a combination of these factors. Obesity is defined as having excess body fat.

- Obese youth are more likely to have risk factors for cardiovascular disease, such as high cholesterol or high blood pressure. In a population-based sample of 5- to 17-year-olds, 70% of obese youth had at least one risk factor for cardiovascular disease.

Source: Centers for Disease Control and Prevention. January 28, 2013. <www.cdc.gov.>

Source 3

School Health Guidelines to Promote Healthy Eating and Physical Activity: Executive Summary

1. Use a coordinated approach to develop, implement, and evaluate healthy eating and physical activity policies and practices.
2. Establish school environments that support healthy eating and physical activity.
3. Provide a quality school meal program and ensure that students have only appealing, healthy food and beverage choices offered outside of the school meal program.
4. Implement a comprehensive physical activity program with quality physical education as the cornerstone.
5. Implement health education that provides students with the knowledge, attitudes, skills, and experiences needed for lifelong healthy eating and physical activity.
6. Provide students with health, mental health, and social services to address healthy eating, physical activity, and related chronic disease prevention.
7. Partner with families and community members in the development and implementation of healthy eating and physical activity policies, practices, and programs.

Source: National Center for Chronic Disease Prevention and Health Promotion. September 2011. <www.cdc.gov.>

Source 4

Learn the Facts: How Did We Get Here?

Thirty years ago, most people led lives that kept them at a healthy weight. Kids walked to and from school every day, ran around at recess, participated in gym class, and played for hours after school before dinner. Meals were home-cooked with reasonable portion sizes, and there was always a vegetable on the plate. Eating fast food was rare and snacking between meals was an occasional treat. Today, children experience a very different lifestyle. Walks to and from school have been replaced by car and bus rides. Gym class and after-school sports have been cut; afternoons are now spent with TV, video games, and the Internet. Parents are busier than ever and

continued on next page

continued from previous page

families eat fewer home-cooked meals. Snacking between meals is now commonplace.

Thirty years ago, kids ate just one snack a day, whereas now they are trending toward three snacks, resulting in an additional 200 calories a day. And one in five school-age children has up to six snacks a day.

Portion sizes have also exploded—they are now two to five times bigger than they were in years past. Beverage portions have grown as well—in the mid-1970s, the average sugar-sweetened beverage was 13.6 ounces compared to today. Kids think nothing of drinking 20 ounces of sugar-sweetened beverages at a time.

In total, we are now eating 31 percent more calories than we were forty years ago—including 56 percent more fats and oils and 14 percent more sugars and sweeteners. The average American now eats fifteen more pounds of sugar a year than in 1970. Eight to 18-year-old adolescents spend an average of 7.5 hours a day using entertainment media, including TV, computers, video games, cell phones and movies, and only one-third of high school students get the recommended levels of physical activity.

Source: Let's Move: America's Move to Raise a Healthier Generation of Kids. <www.letsmove.gov>

Step 3. Organize your ideas.

Your report must be unified and organized. First, write a thesis statement that communicates the main idea of your report. In one sense, your thesis statement is the answer to your research question. The **thesis statement** will guide the content and order of your report. Making an outline before you write your draft will help you organize your ideas.

A research report, like most other types of texts, is organized into three basic parts: The **introduction** should introduce the topic and contain the thesis statement, usually in one paragraph. The **body** should present the research, often in several paragraphs. The **conclusion** should restate the topic and summarize the research. It should give a sense of closure to the writing.

Activity 5C Organizing Information

Draw a line from the topic to the order that best fits with the topic.

Research Report Topics	Possible Orders
Reasons to volunteer	Chronological, time order
Underage drinking	Problem and Solution
Why the United States became involved in the Vietnam War	Compare and Contrast
Causes of the Civil War	Order of importance, least to most important or most to least important
Stages of mitosis, or cell division	

1. Which order would you use if you were writing an essay based on the prompt about obesity from page 57?

_____

Activity 5D Analyzing an Outline

Following is an outline for a research report about childhood obesity. As you read it, mark it as follows:

1. Circle the heading for the portions of the outline that are part of the body.

2. Underline the thesis statement.

3. Are the main points in the body in logical order? Why or why not?

Collaborate About Organization

Before organizing your information, discuss it with a partner. Talking about what you have researched can help you see the best way to organize it.

Organizational Patterns

For more about organization in writing, see page 9.

Sample Outline: America's Obesity Epidemic

I. **Introduction**

    A. American culture promotes obesity.

    B. Childhood obesity has become a national epidemic and can only be solved by changing the American culture.

II. **The Size of the Problem**

    A. Statistics show the magnitude of the problem.

    B. Modern life has made the problem greater.

III. **Solutions for the Problem**

    A. Children must learn to eat healthier.

    B. Children must be more active.

IV. **Conclusion**

    A. Government, schools, religious organizations, and parents must work together to stop the obesity epidemic.

    B. Creating a healthier culture is critical.

Step 4. Write the draft.

On the next page is a draft of the report. It is based on the outline and the notes taken on the sources. You will notice that it contains some errors.

Activity 5E Analyzing a Draft

Following is the draft of an essay. Mark it as follows:

1. In the margin beside the introduction, write a phrase to indicate whether you think it is an effective opening to the report.

2. Write "introduction" beside the introductory paragraph and "conclusion" beside the concluding paragraph.

3. Place a check mark in the margin beside three specific pieces of evidence from the sources.

4. Circle three transitional words or phrases.

5. Draw a box around headings that show the organization of the essay.

6. In the margin at the end of the report, write "yes," "somewhat," or "no" to evaluate whether this report demonstrates understanding of the subject under investigation.

> **Two Special Sentences**
>
> The first and last sentences of a report are particularly important. The first sentence of the introduction should grab the reader's attention. The last sentence of the conclusion should leave a strong impression in the reader's mind.

Sample Draft: America's Obesity Epidemic

There is a silent epidemic attacking children in the United States. If this was a typical epidemic, parents and authorities would be crying out for a solution. But this epidemic is not an infectious disease or a threat of bioterrorism ("Progress" 1). Instead it is a silent killer that slowly but surely kills children over a period of years. Childhood obesity has become a national epidemic that can only be solved by changing the American culture.

The Problem of Obesity

Statistics show the magnitude of the problem. In the last 30 years, obesity has doubled in children and tripled in adolescents. In 2010, the percentage of children ages 6–19 who were obese is nearly 18 percent. More than one-third of American children and adolescents were overweight or obese ("Facts").

The causes of the epidemic are found in the way modern Americans eat and play today. Families are very busy. Usually both parents are working. This means fewer healthy, home-cooked meals and more fast food. Portion sizes are two to five times bigger than they have been in the past. And kids are also eating more snacks. In all, Americans are now consuming "31 percent more calories than we were forty years ago—including 56 percent more fats and oils and 14 percent more sugars and sweeteners.

Americans are consuming more calories, but are less active than in the past. Children used to play outside. Now most children and adolescents spend 7.5 hours a day using entertainment media, including TV, computers, video games, and cell phones. Gym classes and recess have also been cut ("Facts").

Solutions for Obesity

The government, along with nonprofit organizations, have taken up the cause of ending childhood obesity. Most organizations agree that the solution involves changing the way American children eat and play.

School lunches now include more vegetables and fewer sugary desserts. First, children must be educated on how to eat healthier. Schools are teaching children by example. The center for disease

continued on next page

continued from previous page

control has put out School Health Guidelines to Promote Healthy Eating and Physical Activity, which sets out to "Establish school environments that support healthy eating and physical activity" ("Guidelines"). Children are also being taught how to make healthy choices at home. Low-income children are given backpacks of fruits and vegetables to eat at home over the weekend ("Guidelines").

Let's Move! is a comprehensive initiative launched by first lady Michelle Obama. This organization encourages children to be active 60 minutes a day. Through its Web site and public service announcements, the message of turning off technology and getting outside is promoted. Schools are striving to implement physical education classes that introduce students to lifelong physical activities which they can engage in both in school and at home ("Guidelines").

Steps are being taken to stop the obesity epidemic, but it will take a combined effort by the government, schools, community organizations, and parents to reverse the tide. If not, we can look forward to many obese adults who are afflicted with diabetes, high blood pressure, and heart disease. They will drive up health care costs and die early.

Step 5. Revise your essay.

After you write a draft, read it again. Make revisions to improve it. You may need to change the order of information so that it flows more logically. Consider the flow of ideas in the following paragraph:

> **Active and Passive Voice Verbs**
>
> Remember to use active voice verbs as much as possible. Use passive voice verbs when you want to downplay the subject or the subject is unknown.

School lunches now include more vegetables and fewer sugary desserts. First, children must be educated on how to eat healthier. Schools are teaching children by example. The center for disease control has put out School Health Guidelines to Promote Healthy Eating and Physical Activity, which sets out to "Establish school environments that support healthy eating and physical activity" ("Guidelines"). Children are also being taught how to make healthy choices at home. Low-income children are given backpacks of fruits and vegetables to eat at home over the weekend ("Guidelines").

Activity 5F Revising for Logical Order

Use the paragraph on the previous page to complete the following:

1. The main idea of the paragraph is to explain steps being taken to encourage children to eat healthier. Underline the sentence in the paragraph that communicates the main idea.

2. Write "move" next to a sentence that belongs in the previous paragraph about how organizations are changing the way children eat and play.

3. Write a number at the beginning of each sentence to indicate a more logical order.

The tone of writing is the author's attitude toward the topic. For a research report, it is important to maintain an objective, formal **tone**. You may find that you have some strong opinions about a topic, but a research report is not the place to air these opinions.

Activity 5G Revising for Tone

Reread the conclusion of the research report on page 64 and then complete the following:

1. Underline sentences where the tone becomes harsh instead of objective.

2. On the lines below, rewrite the sentences you underlined so that the tone is consistent with the rest of the report. End the report with a good concluding sentence.

> ### Collaboration About Tone
>
> As a writer, you may not be able to identify when your tone becomes opinionated or too informal. Ask a friend to read and evaluate your report and suggest places where the tone is not consistent.

_____

_____

_____

_____

_____

_____

_____

_____

_____

Step 6. Edit and proofread your essay.

After revising your paper, proofread it carefully, looking for mistakes in spelling, punctuation, usage, and grammar. Consider the following sentence:

> If this was a typical epidemic, parents and authorities would be crying out for a solution.

The problem with this sentence relates to the mood of the verb. Verb moods indicate a state of being or reality. The verb in the sentence above is in subjunctive mood. It is communicating something doubtful or not factual. When you express a wish or something that is not actually true, use *were*, not *was*. See the corrected sentence below:

> If this <u>were</u> a typical epidemic, parents and authorities would be crying out for a solution.

 ### Activity 5H Using Subjunctive Mood

Rewrite the following sentences using the correct subjunctive mood verb.

1. If I was you, I would not walk home in this weather.

_____

_____

2. I wish I was able to go to the movies tonight.

_____

_____

3. If that was true, I wouldn't be here today.

_____

_____

 ### Activity 5I Proofreading an Essay

Find and correct the following mistakes in the model essay.

1. Change a verb in present tense to past tense.

2. Add quotation marks to the end of a direct quote. Also add an in-text citation.

3. Capitalize the title of a person and an organization.

Mood and Verbs

Subjunctive mood is just one type of mood. Other verb moods include:

Imperative: Pass me the football. (expresses a command or request)

Indicative: In England, soccer is called football. (expresses a fact)

Interrogative: Where did you throw it? (asks a question)

Conditional: If I throw the ball, I may hit the window. (expresses a conditional state that will cause something to happen)

LESSON 6 YOU TRY IT

Now it is your turn to write a research report. Use the steps outlined in this chapter to guide you as you write.

Activity 6A Writing a Research Report

Write a research report in response to one of the following prompts.

A. Robots in Space	B. Historical Roots of Political Parties
Conduct research on Robonauts, robots created to assist astronauts in space. Explore what Robonauts do and how they work. Gather information from four different sources. Write a report in which you include information from all four sources.	Research the conflict between Thomas Jefferson and Alexander Hamilton during the 1790s. Describe how the men and their parties differed on major issues. Explain how their conflict shaped the political system of the United States today. Cite at least four sources in your report.

Steps for Writing a Research Report

1. Understand the prompt.
2. Take notes on sources.
3. Write a thesis statement and organize your ideas.
4. Write the draft.
5. Revise your essay.
6. Edit and proofread your essay.

Checklist

Use the following checklist to edit your report.

	My writing has . . .
DEVELOPMENT	❏ a clear question to answer or problem to solve ❏ a topic appropriate to the length of the report
ORGANIZATION	❏ a clear introduction, body, and conclusion ❏ good transitions to maintain the flow of ideas ❏ logical order
EVIDENCE	❏ strong, relevant textual evidence ❏ information from multiple authoritative sources
LANGUAGE & STYLE	❏ precise, appropriate word choice ❏ a formal, objective tone
GRAMMAR, SPELLING, & PUNCTUATION	❏ standard grammar ❏ correct spelling ❏ proper punctuation

Writing a Literary Analysis

A **literary analysis** interprets one or more works of literature. It supports that interpretation with appropriate evidence, such as quotations and other details, from the literature. In addition, a literary analysis often includes facts and informed judgments from other sources, such as biographies of the writer or historical works about the events described in the literature.

> **Types of Literature**
>
> Writing assessments may ask you to read and respond to poetry, drama, or a short story.

LESSON 1 ELEMENTS OF A LITERARY ANALYSIS

A literary analysis essay requires you to look at specific elements of a work of literature. Here are some commonly used literary devices found in stories and poems and how you might be asked to write about them in an essay.

Definitions of Literary Elements	A prompt may ask you to analyze how . . .
Characterization: description of the characters in the story	• characters develop and change • characters advance the plot • characters develop the theme
Plot: events in the story	• events in the story influence the characters • the author uses events to create mystery or tension
Structure: arrangement of lines of poetry or the order in which ideas are presented	• the structure supports the theme
Setting: where and when the events take place	• the setting influences the plot and the characters' choices
Tone: author's attitude toward the writing	• the author's choice of words creates the tone
Point of View: who is narrating the events	• point of view influences the story or poem
Theme: central idea of a text	• the theme is developed, shaped, and refined by specific details • two passages on the same topic or with the same theme are similar or different
Figurative Language: similes, metaphors, allusions	• imagery or sound devices convey meaning

> **Collaboration on Figurative Language**
>
> In a small group, develop three examples of each type of figurative language described below.
>
> • A **simile** is a comparison using the words *like* or *as*. Example: Life is *like* baseball.
>
> • A **metaphor** is a comparison that does not use *like* or *as*. Example: Life is a baseball game.
>
> • An **allusion** is a reference to something well-known that may not be clearly stated or explained. Example: He was a Scrooge when it came to buying clothes. (Scrooge is the character in *A Christmas Carol* who is famous for not spending money.)

Activity 1A *Understanding Literary Devices*

Choose a work of literature you have read recently. Complete the following tasks to help you analyze the work.

Title: _____

1. Describe the main characters:

_____

_____

_____

2. Summarize the plot:

_____

_____

_____

_____

_____

3. Describe the setting:

_____

_____

4. Identify the tone:

_____

_____

5. Identify the point of view:

_____

_____

6. Explain the theme:

_____

_____

7. Give examples of two types of figurative language used:

_____

_____

LESSON 2 EVIDENCE FROM TEXTS

Before you write an essay, you will be asked to read a work of literature. Watch for important details in the writing; underline key sentences that describe the characters and reveal the theme of the work.

If you are taking a writing test, you may be asked to answer some questions before you write your essay. Questions may require you to define key words or phrases, write a summary, or find evidence to support the main ideas. Answering these questions correctly will help you accurately interpret the literature in your analysis essay.

 Activity 2A *Answering Questions About a Work of Literature*

The following is from a play about Joan of Arc, a teenage girl who in 1429 claimed to hear voices from God telling her to drive the English out of France. She led the French and their ruler, the Dauphin, to several important victories during the Hundred Years' War but was captured and burnt at the stake by the English. In the following excerpt, Joan asks Robert de Baudricourt for his help. Read and annotate the play. Then answer the questions that follow.

from **Saint Joan,** Scene I
by George Bernard Shaw

STEWARD. Sir: I tell you there are no eggs. There will be none—not if you were to kill me for it—as long as The Maid is at the door.

ROBERT. The Maid! What maid? What are you talking about?

STEWARD. The girl from Lorraine, sir. From Domrémy.

ROBERT. [*rising in fearful wrath*] Thirty thousand thunders! Fifty thousand devils! Do you mean to say that that girl, who had the impudence to ask to see me two days ago, and whom I told you to send back to her father with my orders that he was to give her a good hiding, is here still?

STEWARD. I have told her to go, sir. She won't.

ROBERT. I did not tell you to tell her to go: I told you to throw her out. You have fifty men-at-arms and a dozen lumps of able-bodied servants to carry out my orders. Are they afraid of her?

STEWARD. She is so positive, sir. . . .

ROBERT. [*seizing him by the scruff of the neck*] Positive! Now see here. I am going to throw you downstairs. . . . I am stronger than you are, you fool.   [25]

STEWARD. Sir, sir: you cannot get rid of her by throwing me out. [*Robert has to let him drop. He squats on his knees on the floor, contemplating his master resignedly.*] You see sir, you are much more positive than I am. But so is she.

ROBERT. I am stronger than you are, you fool.

STEWARD. No, sir: it isn't that: it's your strong character, sir. She is weaker than we are: she is only a slip of a girl; but we cannot make her go.

ROBERT. You parcel of curs: you are afraid of her.

continued on next page

continued from previous page

STEWARD. [*rising cautiously*] No sir: we are afraid of you; but she puts courage into us. She really doesn't seem to be afraid of anything. Perhaps you could frighten her, sir . . .

ROBERT. . . . She shall talk to me a bit . . . Shew her the way, you. And shove her along quick.

Joan appears in the turret doorway. She is an able-bodied country girl of 17 or 18, respectably dressed in red, with an uncommon face; eyes very wide apart and bulging as they often do in very imaginative people, a long well-shaped nose with wide nostrils, a short upper lip, resolute but full-lipped mouth, and handsome fighting [50] *chin. She comes eagerly to the table, delighted at having penetrated to Baudricourt's presence at last, and full of hope as to the results. His scowl does not check or frighten her in the least. Her voice is normally a hearty coaxing voice, very confident, very appealing, very hard to resist.*

JOAN. [*bobbing a curtsey*] Good morning, captain squire. Captain: you are to give me a horse and armor and some soldiers, and send me to the Dauphin. Those are your orders from my Lord.

ROBERT. [*outraged*] Orders from your lord! And who the devil may your lord be? Go back to him, and tell him that I am neither duke nor peer at his orders: I am squire of Baudricourt; and I take no orders except from the king.

JOAN. [*reassuringly*] Yes, squire: that is all right. My Lord is the King of Heaven.

ROBERT. Why, the girl's mad. [*To the steward*] Why didn't you tell me so, you blockhead?

STEWARD. Sir: do not anger her: give her what she wants.

JOAN. [*impatient, but friendly*] They all say I am mad until I talk to them, squire. But you see that it is the will of God that you are [75] to do what He has put into my mind.

ROBERT. It is the will of God that I shall send you back to your father with orders to put you under lock and key and thrash the madness out of you. What have you to say to that?

JOAN. You think you will, squire; but you will find it all coming quite different. You said you would not see me; but here I am.

STEWARD. [*appealing*] Yes, sir. You see, sir.

ROBERT. Hold your tongue, you.

STEWARD. [*abjectly*] Yes, sir.

ROBERT. [*to Joan, with a sour loss of confidence*] So you are presuming on my seeing you, are you?

JOAN. [*sweetly*] Yes, squire.

ROBERT. [*feeling that he has lost ground, brings down his two fists squarely on the table, and inflates his chest imposingly to cure the unwelcome and only too familiar sensation*] Now listen to me. I am going to assert myself.

JOAN. [*busily*] Please do, squire. The horse will cost sixteen francs. It is a good deal of money: but I can save it on the armor. I can find a soldier's armor that will fit me well enough: I am very hardy; and I do not need beautiful armor made to my measure [100] like you wear. I shall not want many soldiers: the Dauphin will give me all I need to raise the siege of Orleans.

continued on next page

continued from previous page

ROBERT. [*flabbergasted*] To raise the siege of Orleans!

JOAN. [*simply*] Yes, squire: that is what God is sending me to do. Three men will be enough for you to send with me if they are good men and gentle to me. They have promised to come with me. Polly and Jack and—

ROBERT. Polly!! You impudent baggage, do you dare call squire Bertrand de Poulengey *Polly* to my face?

JOAN. His friends call him so, squire: I did not know he had any other name. Jack—

ROBERT. That is Monsieur John of Metz, I suppose?

JOAN. Yes, squire. Jack will come willingly: he is a very kind gentleman, and gives me money to give to the poor. I think John Godsave will come, and Dick the Archer, and their servants John of Honecourt and Julian. There will be no trouble for you, squire: I have arranged it all: you have only to give the order.

ROBERT. [*contemplating her in a stupor of* [125] *amazement*] Well, I am damned!

JOAN. [*with unruffled sweetness*] No, squire:

God is very merciful; and the blessed saints Catherine and Margaret, who speak to me every day [*he gapes*], will intercede for you. You will go to paradise; and your name will be remembered forever as my first helper.

ROBERT. [*to the steward, still much bothered, but changing his tone as he pursues a new clue*] Is this true about Monsieur de Poulengey?

STEWARD. [*eagerly*] Yes, sir, and about Monsieur de Metz too. They both want to go with her.

ROBERT. [*thoughtful*] Mf! [*He goes to the window, and shouts into the courtyard.*] Hallo! You there: send Monsieur de Poulengey to me, will you? [*He turns to Joan.*] Get out; and wait in the yard.

JOAN. [*smiling brightly at him*] Right, squire. [*She goes out.*]

ROBERT. [*to the steward*] Go with her, you, you dithering imbecile. Stay within call; and keep your eye on her. I shall have her up here again.

STEWARD. Do so in God's name, sir. Think of those hens, the best layers in [150] Champagne; and—

ROBERT. Think of my boot; and take your backside out of reach of it.

Part A

What does the word impudent *mean in these lines from the text?*

> **ROBERT.** Polly!! You **impudent** baggage, do you dare call squire Bertrand de Poulengey *Polly* to my face?
>
> **JOAN.** His friends call him so, squire: I did not know he had any other name. . . .

a. courageous

b. cocky

c. eager

d. angry

> ### Vocabulary
>
> A set of "selected response" questions can help you understand what you have just read. Some tests present them in two parts. The first question asks you to define a key word from the story. The second question asks you to provide context clues that helped you understand the definition.

Part B

Which words or phrases from the text in Part A best help the reader understand the meaning of the word *impudent?*

a. do you dare

b. His friends call him so

c. squire

d. I did not know he had any other name.

Key Idea

The first of a pair of questions might ask you to identify the key idea in a text. A second question might ask you to identify one or more statements that provide evidence for your choice.

Activity 2B Identifying Key Ideas

Circle the best answer to the following questions.

Part A

Which of the following best describes Joan's character based upon this scene?

a. naive and uneducated

b. mystical

c. self-assured

d. mysterious

Draw Evidence from Literary Texts

Writers often indicate their key ideas through the details they choose to include. In detective stories and mysteries, the plot often turns on one little piece of information. If a detail seems odd or unnecessary, ask yourself why the writer took the time to create it.

Part B

Select three pieces of evidence from Saint Joan *that support the answer to Part A.*

a. **STEWARD.** No, sir: it isn't that: it's your strong character, sir. She is weaker than we are: she is only a slip of a girl . . .

b. **STEWARD.** [*rising cautiously*] No sir: we are afraid of you; but she puts courage into us. She really doesn't seem to be afraid of anything.

c. **STEWARD.** She is so positive, sir. . . .

d. *Her voice is normally a hearty coaxing voice, very confident, very appealing, very hard to resist.*

e. **JOAN.** [*bobbing a curtsey*] Good morning, captain squire. Captain: you are to give me a horse and armor and some soldiers, and send me to the Dauphin. Those are your orders from my Lord.

f. **ROBERT.** Why, the girl's mad.

g. **JOAN.** [*with unruffled sweetness*] No, squire: God is very merciful; and the blessed saints Catherine and Margaret, who speak to me every day . . .

LESSON 3 HOW TO WRITE A LITERARY ANALYSIS

A literary analysis essay will ask you to look for specific elements of the text, such as the theme, the characters, the point of view, or the word choice. You will be required to supply textual evidence to support your analysis of the story. The following will help you break down the process of writing a literary analysis into manageable steps.

Step 1. Understand the prompt.

The directions for writing an essay are called the **prompt.** The verbs in it tell you what to do. Here is an example of a prompt:

> Analyze the character of Joan of Arc in the scene from *Saint Joan*. Compare and contrast Robert's and the steward's reaction to Joan and her mission. Support your ideas with evidence from the text.

Activity 3A Analyzing a Prompt

In the prompt above, underline two key words or phrases in each sentence. Then finish the following statements:

1. In my literary analysis, I must

_____

_____

2. The kinds of details I should include in my essay are

_____

_____

_____

Step 2. Take notes on the texts.

As you read *Saint Joan,* you may have underlined some important sentences or written some notes in the margins. Now you return to the story with the prompt in mind.

- Look for clues that reveal Joan's character.
- Find specific examples of how the steward and Robert react to Joan.
- Organize your notes, possibly using a graphic organizer.

The chart on the next page contains examples of graphic organizers that fit with different writing prompts and purposes.

Steps for Writing a Literary Analysis

1. Understand the prompt.
2. Take notes on the texts.
3. Write a thesis statement.
4. Organize your ideas.
5. Develop a complete outline.
6. Write the draft.
7. Revise your essay.
8. Edit and proofread your essay.

Notes on Literary Texts

In nonfiction, the entire text might be from one point of view—that of the author. In short stories and novels, characters each have their own point of view. You may not be sure if any of the characters represent the author's point of view. As part of your notes, keep track of which character is responsible for the information.

Words in the Prompt	Type of Graphic Organizer	Model
• Compare and contrast two texts or characters • Analyze how a filmed production of a drama stays faithful to or departs from the script	Venn diagram	
• Summarize the plot • Analyze the development of the theme	flowchart	
• Determine the theme • Describe a character	web diagram	
• Analyze characters, tone, or word choice	two-column chart	

Activity 3B Organizing Notes

The Venn diagram below compares and contrasts the steward's and Robert's reaction to Joan. Complete the chart by following these steps.

1. Add another detail under Steward's Reaction.

2. Add another detail under Robert's Reaction.

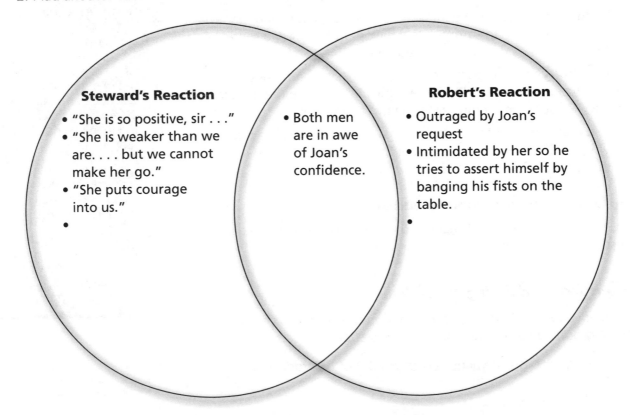

Steward's Reaction

• "She is so positive, sir . . ."
• "She is weaker than we are. . . . but we cannot make her go."
• "She puts courage into us."
•

Both men are in awe of Joan's confidence.

Robert's Reaction

• Outraged by Joan's request
• Intimidated by her so he tries to assert himself by banging his fists on the table.
•

Step 3. Write a thesis statement.

Once you've gathered notes, you should write a thesis statement. The **thesis statement** should clearly state the central idea of your literary analysis. It will guide your writing, so it should fit both the prompt and your notes.

Activity 3C *Write a Thesis Statement*

Finish the sentence to write a strong thesis statement or write your own thesis statement on the lines provided.

1. In this scene from the play, Shaw portrays Joan of Arc as

_____

_____

2. Thesis Statement:

_____

_____

Step 4. Organize your ideas.

Next, think about how you will organize your notes and your thesis statement into a cohesive essay. As you may already know, essays have three main parts: an introduction, a body, and a conclusion.

The **introduction** should include the title of the text and the author. You may want to summarize the work in one or two sentences. You should also include your thesis statement.

In the **body** of your essay, develop your thesis statement by stating your conclusions about the literature. How you organize these main points will depend on the prompt you have been given.

The **conclusion** of the essay brings the writing together in a satisfying way. You may include a final thought. You may also restate your thesis statement using different words.

Step 5. Develop a complete outline.

Before writing your essay, develop an outline to organize the main ideas and supporting details.

Activity 3D *Analyzing an Outline*

Use work you have done for previous activities to help you complete the following outline for a literary analysis essay about Saint Joan.

1. Fill in the thesis statement next to point B of I. Introduction.

> **Ways to Organize a Literary Analysis**
>
> • Comparison/contrast: describe all similarities/ differences of one text and then the other; or, describe one similarity shared by both texts and then one difference between the two texts
>
> • Summaries, Plot analysis, Character analysis: explain examples in chronological order
>
> • Analysis of Word Choice or Theme: organize examples in order of importance (usually least to most important)

2. Fill in subpoints 1 and 2 under points A and B of II. Body. Use textual evidence to support the main points.

3. Restate the thesis statement under point A of III. Conclusion.

Sample Outline: The Inspirational Joan of Arc

I. **Introduction**

    A. *Saint Joan* by George Bernard Shaw is about Joan of Arc and her quest to drive the English out of France.

    B. Thesis Statement: _____

    _____

    _____

II. **Body**

    A. Shaw's Joan is confident, smart, and purposeful.

       1. _____

       _____

       2. _____

       _____

    B. Although both the steward and Robert are in awe of Joan, they respond to her in different ways.

       1. _____

       _____

       2. _____

       _____

III. **Conclusion**

    A. Thesis Statement: _____

    _____

    _____

    B. Although she is only a poor, uneducated girl, her steadfastness of purpose will inspire hundreds of men to follow her into battle.

Including Textual Evidence

The body of your outline should include specific evidence from the text. Evidence may include direct quotations enclosed in quotation marks or paraphrases of the text.

Step 6. Write the draft.

Because you've taken good notes and developed a complete outline, writing your essay will not be difficult. Simply add a few more details to your basic outline. You will also want to include good transitional words and phrases so that the writing flows logically.

Activity 3E Analyzing a Model Essay

Read the following essay. It contains some errors you will correct in a later activity. As you read the essay, complete the following tasks:

1. Underline the thesis statement in the introduction.

2. In the body of the essay, place a check in the margin beside three specific pieces of evidence from the story.

3. Underline two transitional phrases.

4. Identify the conclusion in the margin.

> ### Sample Draft: The Inspirational Joan of Arc
>
> The play *Saint Joan* by George Bernard Shaw is about Joan of Arc and her quest to drive the English out of France. She was made a saint by the Catholic church. In this excerpt from Scene I, the audience is introduced to Joan. The dialogue reveals that Joan is confident and driven. What is most interesting about this scene is how the two male characters—Robert de Baudricourt and his steward—respond differently to Joan.
>
> The audience learns about Joan both from her own words and actions and what other characters say about her. As soon as she enters the scene, she demands, "Captain: you are to give me a horse and armor and some soldiers . . . Those are your orders from my Lord" (1.1.57–61). Her confidence is firmly based in her religious experiences. She gets her direction from God and firmly believes that everyone else will cooperate with her.
>
> The dialogue between Robert and Joan reveal how smart she is. When in a fit of rage Robert bursts out "Well, I am damned," Joan replies that "God is very merciful . . . You will go to paradise: and your name will

Evaluating Writing

Good writing should

- be well developed

- have a cohesive organization

- contain evidence from sources

- use precise language and a formal style

- follow rules of standard grammar, spelling, and punctuation

Verb Tenses in a Literary Analysis

When describing the actions or words of characters in literature, use present tense verbs.

Correct: Joan commands Robert to help her.

Incorrect: Joan commanded Robert to help her.

continued on next page

continued from previous page

be remembered forever as my first helper" (1.1.128–132). This is a good example of Shaw's use of word play—using the word *damned* in two different ways. Robert is merely swearing, but Joan thinks in literal religious terms of being damned to hell.

Although both Robert and his steward are in awe of Joan, they respond to her differently. The steward seems to be mesmerized by Joan. He was suposed to send Joan back to her father. He could not bring himself to use force against her. "She is so positive, sir" he tells Robert (1.1.29). It's not that the steward and the other soldiers are afraid of her (like they are afraid of Robert). The steward says, "she puts courage into us" (1.1.38). The men see this poor, plain girl as a leader who inspires them with her courage.

But Robert is a man who commands soldiers. Before meeting her, he can't fathom that grown men should be intimidated by a girl. Joans frank demands enrage him. For each acousation he makes against her, Joan responds calmly. When he says she is mad, Joan calmly replies, "They all say I am mad until I talk to them . . . But you see that it is the will of God" (1.1.73–75). Robert tries to physically intimidate her by slamming his fists on the table and calling her an "impudent baggage" (1.1.111). The fact that Robert has to say "I am going to assert myself" (1.1.94) shows how futile his attempts to intimidate her have become. Ironically, Robert can easily bully his steward by threatening to throw him down the stairs or kick him in the backside.

In the first scene of his play, Shaw clearly develops the character of Joan of Arc. She is unwaveringly confidence in her mission. Although she is only a poor, uneducated girl, her steadfastness of purpose will inspire hundreds of men to follow her into battle.

> **In-text Citations**
>
> Notice how in-text citations are used to cite lines from literature. For a play, the Act, Scene, and line numbers are recorded. For a shorter poem, the citation may only include the line number. For a book, usually only a page number is needed.

Step 7. Revise your essay.

After you write a draft, revise it to make the content more specific, the ideas more clear, and the writing flow more smoothly. One thing you should think about is how well you use transitions in your writing. Consider the following passage from the model:

Although both Robert and his steward are in awe of Joan, they respond to her differently. The steward seems to be mesmerized by Joan. He was supposed to send Joan back to her father. He could not bring himself to use force against her. "She is so positive, sir" he tells Robert.

This paragraph has very few transitional phrases. Think of transitional phrases as road signs that help the reader follow your train of thought. The following chart shows some common transitional phrases and how they can be used.

Transitional Words/ Phrases	Shows that the next idea is
and, in addition, also, in the same way, likewise, similarly	similar to the previous idea equal in importance
however, on the other hand, in contrast, but, differently, instead	different from the previous idea
as a result, consequently	a result of
because, since	a cause of
first, next, later, after, then, second, third, finally	comes first or later in time
first, second, most importantly, least importantly	is more or less important
a case in point, to illustrate, for example	an example

Notice how the addition of the transitional word *however* clarifies the meaning of the paragraph.

Although both Robert and his steward are in awe of Joan, they respond to her differently. The steward seems to be mesmerized by Joan. He was supposed to send Joan back to her father. <u>However</u>, he could not bring himself to use force against her. "She is so positive, sir" he tells Robert.

Activity 3F Using Transitional Phrases

In the blank, add a transitional phrase to clarify the meaning of the paragraph.

It's not that the steward and the other soldiers are afraid of her like they are afraid of Robert. _____, the steward says, "she puts courage into us" (1.1.38). The men see this poor, plain girl as a leader who inspires them with her courage.

Activity 3G Revising the Model Essay

Complete the following tasks to revise the model essay:

1. Cross out a sentence in the introduction that doesn't fit with the main idea of the paragraph.

2. In the third paragraph, the writer uses the word "smart" to describe Joan. Think of a better adjective to describe her, based upon the evidence used in the rest of the paragraph.

3. Add a transitional word or phrase to help the ideas flow together better.

Step 8. Edit and proofread your essay.

Once you've made your final revisions to the content and the style of your essay, read it again. This time, correct any errors in grammar, punctuation, and spelling.

One type of punctuation that is useful when writing a literary analysis is an ellipsis (. . .). An ellipsis is three evenly spaced periods used to indicate that words are being omitted. Notice the following example:

> When he says she is mad, Joan calmly replies, "They all say I am mad until I talk to them . . . But you see that it is the will of God."

The ellipsis indicates that some words in the quotation are left out. Use an ellipsis when you want to use a direct quotation from a text and you only want to include the information that best supports your argument. Of course, you shouldn't use an ellipsis to make the text say something it doesn't say.

An ellipsis can also be used in dialogue to show a pause in the flow of speech.

> "I was just wondering . . . would you go out with me?" asked Jeff.

Dashes

Dashes can also be used to indicate a pause in the flow of speech, but while an ellipsis indicates that the speech slowly trails off, a dash implies an abrupt cutoff.

"I was just—oh never mind," said Jeff.

Activity 3H Using Ellipses

Follow the instructions to use ellipses in the sentences below.

1. Rewrite the following lines, omitting the second and third sentences about the cost of the horse.

JOAN. Please do, squire. The horse will cost sixteen francs. It is a good deal of money: but I can save it on the armor. I can find a soldier's armor that will fit me well enough: I am very hardy; and I do not need beautiful armor made to my measure like you wear.

_____

_____

_____

_____

2. Rewrite the following lines, omitting the information from *I think* to *Julian*.

JOAN. Yes, squire. Jack will come willingly: he is a very kind gentleman, and gives me money to give to the poor. I think John Godsave will come, and Dick the Archer, and their servants John of Honecourt and Julian. There will be no trouble for you, squire: I have arranged it all: you have only to give the order.

_____

_____

_____

> ### How to Make an Ellipsis
>
> Ellipses are always three dots with a single space between each. If you are omitting something that comes after a period, put the period at the end of the sentence as normal, type a space, and then type your ellipsis. See the example below.
>
> "Please do, squire. . . . I am very hardy."

3. Write a sentence using an ellipsis to show a pause in dialogue.

_____

_____

Activity 3I Proofreading an Essay

In the margin of the model essay, make the following corrections.

1. Find and change two misspelled words.

2. In the fifth paragraph, insert a missing apostrophe to show ownership.

3. In the third paragraph, find a verb that doesn't agree with its subject.

LESSON 4 YOU TRY IT

Now it is your turn to write a literary analysis. Use the steps outlined in this chapter and listed to the right.

Activity 4A *Writing a Literary Analysis*

Choose one of the following prompts and write a literary analysis using the steps outlined in this chapter. Then use the checklist to make sure your writing conforms to the Characteristics of Good Writing.

A. Analyzing a Poem	B. Analyzing Literature
Read the poem "O Captain! My Captain!" by Walt Whitman. Analyze how structure, word choice, and figures of speech support the theme. Support your ideas with evidence from the text.	Choose a work of literature you have read recently and write an essay analyzing how the theme of the work is developed through the plot, characters, point of view, and/or word choice.

Steps for Writing a Literary Analysis

1. Understand the prompt.
2. Take notes on the sources.
3. Write a thesis statement.
4. Organize your ideas.
5. Develop a complete outline.
6. Write the draft.
7. Revise your essay.
8. Edit and proofread your essay.

Checklist

Use the following checklist to edit your essay.

My writing has . . .	
DEVELOPMENT	❏ a clear thesis statement ❏ strong supporting points ❏ addressed all the requirements of the prompt
ORGANIZATION	❏ a clear introduction, body, and conclusion ❏ good transitions ❏ logical order
EVIDENCE	❏ strong, relevant textual evidence ❏ direct quotations or paraphrased information from other texts
LANGUAGE & STYLE	❏ precise, appropriate word choice ❏ a formal, objective tone
GRAMMAR, SPELLING, & PUNCTUATION	❏ standard grammar ❏ correct spelling ❏ proper punctuation

Chapter 6
Writing a Narrative

A **narrative** is a text that tells a story. The story can be either true or imagined, but it is always based on a problem, a situation, or an observation.

LESSON 1 POINT OF VIEW

Narratives come in many forms. Scientists, historians, journalists, and writers of fiction all use narratives to tell how something happened. Following are some examples of narratives:

- a novel such as *The Hunger Games,* by Suzanne Collins

- a chapter in a book telling the story of Nelson Mandela and his quest to end apartheid in South Africa

- a science fiction short story you wrote about a dystopian world where people live in domes because of the extreme weather patterns

- a one-page account of your efforts to train your new puppy

The person telling a story is the narrator. If the narrator participates in the events and describes what happens from his or her point of view, the story is a first-person narrative. If the narrator is not a participant, but is telling readers about other people, the story is a third-person narrative.

> **Pronoun Clues and Point of View**
>
> A first-person narrator often uses *I, we, me, us, my,* and *our.* A third-person narrator often uses *he, she, they, his, her, their,* and *them.*

Activity 1A Identifying the Point of View

Place a check mark in the column to indicate whether each passage is written in first person or third person. Write one or more clue words that you used to make your choice.

Passage	First Person	Third Person	Clue Words
1. Eduardo quickly scanned the poster, searching for the date of the festival. "It's this Saturday," he said to himself.			
2. So far as I can now recall, the first knowledge I got of the fact that we were slaves, and that freedom of slaves was being discussed was early one morning . . .			
3. Every time Mr. Daley heard the doorbell ring, he felt his heart start to race.			
4. We skirted around the south edge of the lake and followed the trail that disappeared into the woods.			

LESSON 2 NARRATIVE TECHNIQUES

Narrative writers use a variety of techniques to describe experiences, explain why events happened, and to portray characters. For example:

- The **narrator** is the person telling the events in the story. In a personal narrative, you are the narrator. In a short story, you may choose one of the characters or an outside voice to describe the events. Your choice of narrator influences the point of view of the story and whether your readers get the perspective of multiple characters or just one person.

- **Context, or setting,** is where the events are taking place. The setting often drives the events in the story and creates the mood.

- **Dialogue** consists of words spoken by characters in the story. These words are enclosed in quotation marks. Dialogue helps characters come alive for readers.

- **Description** includes specific details about people, things, and events. These details help the reader imagine what the writer is portraying.

- **Reflection** occurs when a character or the narrator thinks about and comments on what has happened. Reflection helps the readers understand how characters view events in the narrative.

> **Pacing**
>
> A skilled writer of narrative controls the pacing. **Pacing** is how quickly events occur in a story. In a fast-paced story, events rush by. In a slow-paced story, the writer takes more time for description and reflection. Writers often adjust the pacing as a way to control the tension in the story.

 ### Activity 2A Identifying Techniques

In the following paragraphs, underline and identify examples of setting, dialogue, description, and reflection. An example of narration has been done for you.

<u>My most treasured item is the baseball glove my grandfather gave me.</u> My grandfather was a big man with a mane of silver hair and blue eyes that lit up every time the subject of baseball was mentioned. He instilled a love of baseball in me when I was only about five. He'd take me out in the backyard and pitch plastic balls to me, and I would stand with my Cubs hat on backward, hold the oversized red bat in my hands, and swing away. As I remember, I spent more time chasing the ball after I missed it than I did actually hitting it.

"That's okay, buddy," Grandpa would say. "You'll get the next one."

Then, one morning when I was seven, Grandpa called to tell me he had a surprise for me and he was coming right over. . . .

First-person narrator

LESSON 3 SEQUENCE OF EVENTS

As the writer, you decide the order in which to present the events in a narrative.

- Presenting events in the order they occurred helps readers follow the story easily. This type of organization is called **chronological order.**

- Starting in the middle of a dramatic event can be a good way to grab the attention of the readers. If you start in the middle of the story, you may want to use flashback to share events that led up to the current crisis.

- Starting with the final result of a series of events encourages the reader to focus on the process that led up to the result.

Whichever order you use, you need to make your story coherent. **Coherent** means that each idea is connected to the one before and after it. Use transitional words, phrases, and clauses to signal shifts in time or settings.

> **Selecting Events**
>
> One of a writer's first decisions is to select which events to include. For example, on most days what you ate for breakfast might be unimportant. However, if you ate something unusual that reflected a change in your life, breakfast might be a significant event.

Activity 3A Identifying Transitional Phrases

Underline four transitional phrases in the following paragraph that help you understand when and where the story is taking place.

> "What a bummer!" Juan thought to himself. He had broken his leg in a skiing accident last weekend. Now his leg was in a cast and he would have to stay at home for several weeks until it healed. Sitting on his couch, he looked out the window and watched his neighbor Wendy open her garage door. Inside the garage was a large mound covered with burlap sacks. Wendy looked around carefully. Then she quickly went inside and closed the garage door. "That's strange," thought Juan.

> **Narrative Transitional Phrases**
>
> Since a narrative describes events, use transitional phrases that relate to time, such as *first, later that day, now,* and *afterward.* Transitional phrases may also relate to where the action is taking place: *down the block, at the beach,* or *at school.*

Activity 3B Writing a Coherent Paragraph

Write a short paragraph about the events of a bad day. Underline the transitional phrases you use.

_____

_____

_____

_____

_____

LESSON 4 DESCRIPTIVE LANGUAGE

When you write, choose clear, vivid words to express exactly what you mean.

- Use precise words and phrases rather than general ones. *Frigid* conveys more information than *very cold.*

- Use details that tell something significant about a person, thing, or event. Good writers show instead of tell. For example, saying your mom's eye began to twitch is more interesting than saying she was starting to get mad.

- Use **sensory words,** words that appeal to the five senses: sight, hearing, taste, smell, and touch. Phrases such as *the sad brown of downtrodden leaves* or *stinky as tennis shoes left to bake in the sun* impress your ideas on readers.

> ### Finding Vivid Words
>
> Use the thesaurus feature of your word processor to suggest vivid words you can use to replace vague words. Keep a list of new words you see in your reading or hear people say. To help you learn these new words, use them as soon as you can find a time that is appropriate.

Activity 4A *Using Precise Words and Phrases*

For each general word, write two words or phrases that are more precise.

General Word	More Precise Words or Phrases	
1. walk		
2. house		

Activity 4B *Using Sensory Language*

Write a one-paragraph narrative about a party or other event you attended recently. Underline five examples of sensory language.

_____

_____

_____

_____

_____

_____

_____

LESSON 5 CONCLUSION

Like other types of writing, a narrative ends with a conclusion. In a narrative, the conclusion typically gives the reader a sense that the story is complete. The conclusion

- should follow from the rest of the narrative, wrapping up any loose ends

- might include reflections on what happened in the narrative, putting the story into a broader context

In a text that is only a page or two long, the conclusion might be only a sentence. In a twenty-chapter novel, the conclusion might be the last chapter.

Activity 5A Writing a Conclusion

Write a one-paragraph conclusion for a narrative retelling an incident from a well-known story, such as a fairy tale or a famous historical event.

Incident: _____

_____

_____

_____

_____

_____

_____

_____

_____

_____

_____

_____

_____

_____

_____

_____

> **Collaboration About a Conclusion**
>
> If you are having trouble writing a strong conclusion, talk about what you might write with a classmate. If no classmate is available, pretend you are talking with a friend. Many people find that talking aloud helps them clarify what to write.

LESSON 6 HOW TO WRITE A NARRATIVE

Following is a model demonstrating the six steps in writing a narrative essay. Use these six steps to help you in writing your own essays.

Step 1. Understand the prompt.

The directions for writing a narrative essay are called the **prompt.**

Activity 6A Analyzing the Prompt

Read the following prompt. Underline three important elements that your essay should include.

> Write a fictional first-person narrative based on the incident described in the primary source provided below. In the source, Mary Henry, a resident of Washington, D.C., during the Civil War, describes the assassination of President Lincoln. Choose a real or fictional character and describe the events from his or her point of view. For example, you may choose to describe the events from the perspective of Mrs. Lincoln, Dr. Gurley, or a member of the audience at Ford's Theater. While you can create dialogue and other details from your imagination, your story should be consistent with Henry's account of the event.

Step 2. Take notes on the sources.

Below is an excerpt from a journal kept by Mary Henry during April of 1865. Use it to practice taking notes.

Activity 6B Taking Notes

Read the following excerpt once so that you understand the basic story. Then reread it, underlining key ideas and adding comments alongside the text to help you analyze the development of the narrative. Because it is a primary source, it contains some grammatical errors.

Writing a Narrative Essay

1. Understand the prompt.

2. Take notes on the sources.

3. Organize your ideas.

4. Write the draft.

5. Revise your narrative.

6. Edit and proofread your narrative.

Historical Narratives

Sometimes when writing a historical narrative, it is helpful to do further research in order to fill in details of your story. For example, you might find other witnesses' accounts of Lincoln's assassination or death.

Source 1

Death of Abraham Lincoln, April 15
by Mary Henry

[April] 15. We were awakened this morning by an announcement which almost made our hearts stand still with consternation. The President was shot last night in the Theater. . . . It was announced in yesterday's papers that the President with Gen Grant would be at Ford's Theater in the evening and a large crowd collected there in consequence. Gen Grant however left the city before night for N.Y. Mrs.

continued on next page

continued from previous page

Lincoln had not been well and the President went to the place of amusement with reluctance, not wishing to disappoint the audience. He was received with more than usual applause. About 9 1/2 o'clock a shot was heard which was at first supposed to be from the stage and a man leaped from the President's box upon the stage crying "Sic semper Tyrannis" "I have done it." and making his way to the door mounted a horse & rode off. The shrieks of Madame Lincoln first announced to the petrified audience the catastrophe which had taken place. The President was found to be in a state of insensibility, shot twice through the head. He was immediately conveyed to a house opposite the theatre followed by Mrs. L. escorted by her friends in almost a frantic condition.

[April] 18th. . . . I went to see Dr. & Mrs. Gurley [the minister at President Lincoln's church] yesterday afternoon. The Dr. said he had been called to go to the President about 4 o'clock in the morning. He found him in the house opposite the theatre lying insensible upon a bed with the life blood dripping from the wound in his head upon the clothes on the floor beneath. The several members of the Cabinet & other persons were standing around, the deepest sorrow depicted upon their countenances. The Dr. went to the bed side for a while, but was much too overcome with his feelings to perform the religious services required of him. He went to Mrs. Lincoln and found her in almost frantic condition. The President died at 7 1/2 o'clock. Dr. Gurley returned to his bed side a few minutes before his decease. He made his way through the sorrowing & silent spectators & found him slowly drawing his breath at long intervals lying as before perfectly motionless. A faint hardly perceptible motion in his throat and all was over. So still was the room that the ticking of the President's watch was distinctly heard. After a solemn & impressive prayer, Dr. Gurley went to break the sad intelligence to Mrs. Lincoln who was in the parlor below. She cried out "Oh why did you not tell me he was dying?"

Step 3. Organize your ideas.

Create an outline of the basic events in the story as described by Mary Henry. Include notes that describe the tone of what happened.

Time Lines for Narratives

For a narrative essay, you might use a time line instead of a flowchart. A time line will help you keep events in order.

> **Sample Outline: Dark Morning**
>
> Narrator: Dr. Gurley
> 1. The minister is awakened at 4 o'clock in the morning.
> 2. He is summoned to the President and is anxious to find out what is happening.

> 3. He arrives at the house where Lincoln is.
> 4. He describes the blood on the bed and the solemnness of the room and is overcome with emotion.
> 5. Dr. Gurley goes to comfort Mrs. Lincoln.
> 6. He witnesses Lincoln's death.

> 7. Dr. Gurley tells Mrs. Lincoln that her husband is dead.
> 8. He reflects upon how the country will go forward with reconciliation without their leader.

Activity 6C Analyzing the Outline

On the outline above, make the following notes:

1. Write "introduction," "body," or "conclusion" in the margin beside each of the three main sections.

2. Circle a place in the notes that indicates the tone the writer wants to express.

3. Write "climax" in the margin beside the place where the conflict is resolved.

4. Write "reflection" in the margin beside the place where the narrator reflects on what has happened.

5. Write "description" in the margin beside one place where good description will be important.

Step 4. Write the draft.

Using your notes and your outline, write your essay. The following sample draft includes errors that you will correct in later activities.

Sample Draft: Dark Morning

My dreams were dark. I can only remember the faintest details now, but I recall being in the back of a wagon pulled by horses galloping along at full speed. There was no driver, and I was desperately trying to grab the reigns while holding on for dear life. Suddenly, the wagon wheels began to bump over ruts in the road, louder and louder the noise increased in volume until I woke with a start. Someone was knocking on our door.

I threw on some clothes and hurried downstairs as Eliza, our maid, let the poor fellow inside. He gave few details but said I was needed by the President. The clock struck four as I hurried upstairs to dress. I wondered why the President would send for me, his minister and spiritual counselor, in the middle of the night.

Instead of taking me to the White House, the carriage turned toward Ford's Theater. I knew the Lincolns had attended the performance there the night before, all the papers had recorded it. When the driver stopped in front of the house across from the theater, my heart sank. Had Mr. Lincoln taken ill during the performance?

The little parlor of the house was crowded with people speaking in low voices. Above the murmur, I heard Mrs. Lincoln, wailing incomprehensible phrases while several cabinet members' wives tried to calm her. In a tiny room in the back of the house lay the President. I was shocked by the blood—so much blood from his wounded head—staining the pillow, the bedclothes, even the floor—crimson. I confessed I was

continued on next page

continued from previous page

so overwhelmed that I couldn't pray, I couldn't whisper words of comfort or hope. I turned from the horrible sight and pushed my way out of the room. I went to Mrs. Lincoln. She seemed not to understand the gravity of the President's condition.

"Shot . . . shot in head. He had a premonition about this . . . He foresaw this happening . . . Did you see him, Dr. Gurley? How shall I ever feel safe again? Shot in the middle of the play. Did you speak with him? It can't be . . . Oh it can't be—"

I tried to comfort her as best I could and somehow was able to whisper a prayer for her poor husband, although I believed that she needed it more than he did. In my heart I knew that the President was not long for this world.

At a quarter after seven, I was sent for again, pulling myself together, I slipped through the crowd of people in the tiny bedroom. The President was motionless, still, and ghostly pale. Occasionally he would draw a slow, shallow breath. Then he lay still. Seconds passed . . . another shallow breath. "Yea, though I walk through the valley of the shadow of death . . ."

Another rattling breath slipped through his dry lips.

". . . I will fear no evil . . ."

A gurgle of air escaped his throat and it was over. A deathly stillness had fallen over the room. Not a soul spoke a word, no cries of mourning or sobbing. Just silent tears running down stoney cheeks. The only sound was the tick, tick, tick of the President's watch. How could time march on when the world had lost one of its very best men?

"Our Father, we turn to you in this time of loss. . ." My instincts took over, and I prayed beside

continued on next page

continued from previous page

Lincoln's body. I'm sure I spoke words of comfort. I don't remember now. I only recall the heaviness in my chest as my heart shattered.

It fell to me to tell Mrs. Lincoln of the news of her husband's death. I found her sitting more quietly than before. Her eyes closed, her head thrown back on the chair. I went to her and took her hand, breaking the news to her as gently as I could. I'll never forget the look of agony and despair on her face as she cried out, "Oh, why did you not tell me he was dying?" She immediately started up and pushed through the crowd, crying out hysterically for her husband.

Stepping outside, I found the morning was gray and cloudy. As the dark clouds of grief descended upon our city and our country, I wondered how our nation could go forth now that our wise leader was no longer here to guide us.

Activity 6D Evaluating the Draft

Mark the following comments on the draft:

1. Circle two transition words that connect sentences effectively.

2. Underline three examples of precise words or phrases.

3. Place a check mark in the margin beside two examples of sensory language.

Step 5. Revise your narrative.

After you write a draft, read it again carefully. Make revisions to improve the effectiveness of the writing. You will want to make sure your sentences are varied. Using verbals in your writing is one way to make sure your writing is interesting. Verbals are words that look like verbs, but they are used as nouns, adjectives, and adverbs. Here are some examples of the three types of verbals: gerunds, participles, and infinitives.

> **Participle used as an adjective:** I went to her and took her hand, <u>breaking</u> the news to her as gently as I could.

> **Infinitive used as the subject:** <u>To watch</u> a President die is a horrible thing.

> **Gerund used as the subject:** The <u>banging</u> on the door woke me up.

> ### Verbals Phrases
>
> Verbals may be one word, or they may appear in phrases and have objects and modifiers. All of the verbals in the examples to the left are part of longer verbal phrases.

Activity 6E Writing with Verbals

Write sentences using verbals by following the instructions below.

1. Use the infinitive *to walk* as the subject of a sentence.

_____

_____

_____

2. Use the participle *flying* as an adjective in a sentence.

_____

_____

_____

Step 6. Edit and proofread your narrative.

After you write a draft, read it again carefully. Make corrections to improve the effectiveness of the writing. You should follow norms and conventions regarding spelling, punctuation, grammar, and usage. What mistake is made in the following excerpt from the model essay?

> Suddenly, the wagon wheels began to bump over ruts in the road, louder and louder the noise increased in volume until I woke with a start. Someone was knocking loudly on our door.

The following sentence is a run-on, or two sentences written together with only a comma joining them. This is also called a *comma splice*. The first sentence ends after the word *road*. This error can be easily fixed by replacing the comma with a period.

> Suddenly, the wagon wheels began to bump over ruts in the road. Louder and louder the noise increased in volume until I woke with a start. Someone was knocking loudly on our door.

Activity 6F Correcting Run-on Sentences

Fix the following run-on sentences by rewriting them as two sentences.

1. I knew the Lincolns had attended the performance the night before, all the papers had recorded it.

   _____

   _____

   _____

2. A quarter after seven, I was sent for again, pulling myself together, I slipped through the crowd of people in the tiny bedroom.

   _____

   _____

   _____

Pauses and Run-on Sentences

Reading a text aloud can help you identify run-on sentences. Since people naturally pause at the end of each sentence when they talk, listen for the pauses. However, when people are too excited to take a breath, they sometimes speak in run-on sentences.

Correcting Run-on Sentences

Other ways to correct run-on sentences include

- joining the sentences with a comma and a conjunction (*and, but, for, nor*)

- joining the sentences with a semicolon

LESSON 7 YOU TRY IT

Now it is your turn to write a narrative. Use the steps outlined in this chapter and listed to the right.

Activity 7A *Writing a Narrative*

Choose one of the following prompts and write a narrative in response to it.

A. Standing Against Injustice	B. Writing a Sequel
Write a narrative about a time when you (or an imagined character) took a stand against injustice or tried to defend someone being treated unfairly. The events may be based upon your own life, or you may choose to write a fictional narrative based upon a historical event.	Select a short story from a textbook, library book, or online source. Write a one-page sequel to it, focusing on what happens to one of the characters in the story.

Writing a Narrative Essay

1. Understand the prompt.
2. Take notes on the sources.
3. Organize your ideas.
4. Write the draft.
5. Revise your narrative.
6. Edit and proofread your narrative.

Checklist

Use the following checklist to edit your narrative.

My writing has . . .	
DEVELOPMENT	❏ a clear experience or event to tell ❏ narrative techniques to develop experiences, events, and characters
ORGANIZATION	❏ a problem, situation, or observation to engage the reader ❏ a clear introduction, body, and conclusion ❏ good transitions to maintain the flow of ideas ❏ events that build on one another to create a coherent whole
EVIDENCE	❏ well-chosen details ❏ well-structured event sequences
LANGUAGE & STYLE	❏ precise words and phrases ❏ telling details ❏ sensory language
GRAMMAR, SPELLING, & PUNCTUATION	❏ standard grammar ❏ correct spelling ❏ proper punctuation

Tips for Success

LESSON 1 TEN TIPS FOR QUICK REVISION

You may not have much time to revise an essay on a test. As a result, you will want to decide quickly what to fix. Here is a list of actions to take.

☐ 1. Reread your main idea carefully. It should be stated precisely and clearly.

☐ 2. Compare your introduction and your conclusion. They should both address the main idea.

☐ 3. Be sure your body paragraphs have enough details, such as relevant evidence, well-chosen facts, precise words, and sensory language.

☐ 4. Check for appropriate and varied transitions between paragraphs and between sentences.

☐ 5. Read your essay silently, but slowly, word-by-word, as if you were giving a speech. Revise any awkward words or phrases.

☐ 6. Look for words you might have omitted or written twice.

☐ 7. Check the style and tone of the essay. Usually, you should use a formal style and objective tone.

☐ 8. Check that each pronoun refers clearly to a noun and is used correctly.

☐ 9. Insert commas where they are necessary. Delete commas where they are not.

☐ 10. Correct any misspelled words. If you are writing your essay on a computer, some of these may be highlighted by the word processing program.

Types of Main Ideas

Depending on the type of essay you are writing, your main idea might be a

• claim to support

• topic to examine

• situation to explain

• problem to solve

• question to answer

Corrections by Hand

If you are writing your essay by hand, make any changes neatly. Use a caret (^) to indicate where you are inserting text.

Activity 1A Applying the Tips

Below is an essay in response to the prompt, "Explain whom you admire most." Using the tips on page 98, decide if each underlined section is correct as is or needs revision. Write correct *in the margin if no change is needed. If the section is incorrect, make the needed change. Next to each underlined section, write the number of the tip that applies. Not all tips will be used.*

To a lot of people today, World War II seems like it happened a thousand years ago. But at my great-grandmother's house, the war is still very real. On her wall, she has photographs of relatives who died at the hands of the Nazis—36 in all. On her coffee table, she has a scrapbook of newspaper clippings about the war. And in her mind, she has memories of spending two years in Treblinka, a Nazi concentration camp. (1) <u>The person I admire most is my great-grandmother, Sarah Stein.</u>

(2) <u>First of all,</u> I admire Grandma Sarah because she actually survived the camp. She was sent there when she was only 15 years old. She was in the camp for two years. She did hard labor 14 hours a day. She saw thousands of other prisoners die. But my great-grandmother made up her mind when she entered the camp that she would survive. She told me once that the secret to her survival was not to draw attention to herself. (3) <u>Keeping her eyes down, doing her work, her nightmare would be over soon she kept reminding herself.</u>

I also admire Grandma Sarah because once she left the camp, she was able to make a new life for herself. After the Americans liberated Treblinka, she got a job. She saved her money and came to the United States when she was (4) <u>I don't know, maybe 21 years old.</u> Here, she met my great-grandfather. They got married and spent their lives raising three kids and running a (5) <u>restarant.</u> I don't think everyone who went through what she went through would be able to do that.

(6) <u>Secondly,</u> I admire my great-grandmother because she doesn't feel sorry (7) <u>for for</u> herself. She went through one of the most horrible experiences ever. She doesn't dwell (8) <u>on the past and she</u> doesn't let it stop her from living a good life. She told me that she keeps (9) <u>stuff</u> around to remind her and everyone else what happened so that (10) <u>it</u> doesn't happen again.

I admire my great-grandmother because she survived a concentration camp and made a wonderful life for herself. I'm proud to be named after her.

LESSON 2 GENERAL TEST-TAKING TIPS

Each chapter in this book offers tips and strategies that will help you in all writing that you do. The following five tips are particularly useful for writing well on a test.

❐ 1. Before the test, if you feel nervous, prepare yourself to concentrate. Close your eyes or focus on something that is not distracting. Take several slow, deep breaths. Remind yourself to relax.

❐ 2. Begin the test by quickly previewing all the prompts. This will tell what the test is about and how many texts you will write.

❐ 3. Read each prompt carefully. Locate key words or phrases that will help you find the subject of the assignment.

❐ 4. Plan your time for each task. Allow a few minutes at the beginning of each task for prewriting and a few minutes at the end for revising. Use most of the time for writing.

❐ 5. As you begin to respond to each prompt, organize your thoughts about the topic. Use graphic organizers or outlines if they help you get your thoughts down quickly. Then begin writing.

> **Finish Writing Before You Edit**
>
> Plan to save time to revise your writing. However, don't stop writing to revise. Finishing all tasks is more important than revising any single one.

 Activity 2A Summarizing the General Tips

Summarize each of the five tips listed above into single words or short phrases.

1. _____

2. _____

3. _____

4. _____

5. _____

Activity 2B Writing About a Test

Write a short narrative about a student writing an essay on a test.
Include the five words or phrases you wrote in the previous activity.
Circle these words or phrases.

_____

_____

_____

_____

_____

_____

_____

_____

_____

_____

_____

_____

_____

_____

_____

_____

_____

_____

_____

_____

_____

_____

_____

_____

Memory Devices

Connecting the test-taking tips in a story makes them easier to remember. Similarly, which set of words do you think is easier to remember?

- tests year school start students take often to the

- students often take tests to start the school year

The words are the same in both sets. However, since those in the second set are presented in the order of a single sentence, they arc easier to remember. If you want to remember a set of key words, combine them into a sentence or short story.

LESSON 3 TIPS FOR SPEAKING AND LISTENING

Like reading, listening is a way to gather information. Like writing, speaking is a way to share what you know and think. The following list of tips will help you speak and listen effectively.

☐ 1. Prepare for a discussion by planning what you want to say. Know the evidence you want to refer to that supports your point.

☐ 2. Follow the rules of the discussion. Understand how often you should speak and how long you can speak.

☐ 3. Ask specific questions of other individuals in the discussion. Answer questions asked of you.

☐ 4. Review key ideas. Reflect on what they mean and practice paraphrasing them.

☐ 5. Identify a speaker's claims. Distinguish those that are supported by reasons and evidence and those that are not.

☐ 6. Interpret any images, graphics, or music that a speaker uses.

☐ 7. When presenting your idea orally, use appropriate eye contact, adequate volume, and clear pronunciation.

☐ 8. Use multimedia components, such as graphics, images, music, and sound, in your presentation.

☐ 9. Adapt your presentation to the context and the task.

> **Evaluating Speaking and Listening Skills**
>
> To become more familiar with the tips presented on this page, apply them to discussions held by others. Listen to a panel discussion on a television show. Evaluate how well the participants followed the tips.

Activity 3A Engaging in Discussion

Participate in a small group discussion about a topic about which you have or can gather much solid information. When your group is done, answer these questions about your discussion.

1. How well did members of the group refer to evidence on the topic?

_____

2. How polite were members of the group toward each other?

_____

3. How well did members of the group ask and respond to specific questions raised in the discussion?

_____

Activity 3B Interpreting Speeches

Take notes as you listen to a video of a speech or lecture on the Internet that presents an argument. Then answer the following questions about what you heard.

1. What was the speaker's argument? Identify the specific claims made by the speaker.

   _____

   _____

   _____

2. What reasons and evidence did the speaker provide to support his or her claims?

   _____

   _____

   _____

   _____

3. Explain whether you think the reasons and evidence supported the specific claims strongly or not.

   _____

   _____

   _____

   _____

> **Collaboration on Speaking and Listening**
>
> Practice your speaking and listening skills with a partner. Discuss a topic of mutual interest for two minutes. Then summarize what the other person has said. Check that each of you has spoken your ideas clearly and has listened accurately.

Activity 3C Practicing a Speech

Have a friend videotape you as you present a one-minute excerpt from a famous speech. Review the videotape together and evaluate your speech on these issues:

1. Did you use appropriate eye contact?

   _____

2. Did you speak loudly enough to be heard easily?

   _____

3. Was your pronunciation clear?

   _____